The Gasmak

Fear Lasta Lampaí – Gaillimh 1928

Máirtín Ó Direáin

Ní raibh sé mór an fear
Níor dheas a bhí ach gránna,
Is cóip an bhaile mhóir
Ag fonóid faoi gan náire,
Ach ghluais gan mhairg fós
Is ar chuaill í chuaigh in airde,
Ba draíodóir an fear beag
A raibh an solas ina ghlaic,
É ag tabhairt na gile leis
Ó lampa go lampa sráide.

The Lamplighter – Galway 1928

Not tall, this man
Nor handsome, far from it,
Mocked by the jeering locals
Unfeeling, unashamed.
Ignoring them, he carries on,
Stiffly ascending to each lamp.
A magician, this small man,
With light in his giving,
On his way, spreading brightness,
From each street-lamp in the town.

(Translation by Michael J. Boyle)

Lighting the gas lamp in Enniskillen. Richard Lally, an employee at the gasworks, checks the lamp, watched by a member of the Royal Irish Constabulary.

The Gasmakers

HISTORICAL PERSPECTIVES

ON THE

IRISH GAS INDUSTRY

CHARLES J O'SULLIVAN

THE O'BRIEN PRESS

IRISH GAS ASSOCIATION

First published 1987 by The O'Brien Press
20 Victoria Road, Dublin 6, Ireland.

British Library Cataloguing in Publication Data
The gasmakers: historical perspectives on the Irish gas industry.
I. Gas industry – Ireland – History
338.4'76657'09417   TP733.I73
ISBN 0-86278-143-4 pbk

10   9   8   7   6   5   4   3   2   1

Cover design: Michael O'Brien
Typesetting: Design and Art Facilities Ltd.
Printing: Irish Elsevier Printers, Shannon.

The Author and Publisher would like to
thank Finbarr O'Connell, Declan
O'Connell, Mrs Olive Andrews and
The Gas World for the photographs used in
this book.

Cover photograph: Clonmel *circa* 1850s. Barge delivering coal for
gasmaking and lamplighter lighting the gas lamp. Photograph taken by
Dr William Despard Hempel.

Contents

Foreword

With the possible exception of municipal water supplies, no urban service has a longer history than that of gas. From the early years of the nineteenth century, most Irish towns of any consequence had a gas supply system, based on gas which was manufactured in the works and distributed throughout the town by means of underground pipes, in a variety of materials ranging from wood to asbestos to plastics (latterly) as well as many varieties of iron and steel.

Equally varied was the range of uses to which gas was put. These evolved from street-lighting to lighting of homes, then to domestic cooking. In the twentieth century, electric lighting took over while the use of gas was extended to home heating, as well as being put to specialist industrial uses. In recent years, with the adoption of natural gas, the manufacturing step was rendered obsolete, and the works are now no more than historical curiosities. The range of uses for gas has now broadened to include those of transport fuels, chemical feedstock and industrial processing. Indeed, we think of gas today not just as a fuel, but as a vital component of our total energy supplies.

Thus the Irish gas industry can look back with some pride at its service to the community over the past century and a half. However, 1987 is particularly significant, for it was just one hundred years ago that the first formal association of gas industry professionals was established. It too has evolved over time, and today is known as the Irish Gas Association. We are particularly proud of the fact that it is an all-Ireland body, drawing its membership from Northern Ireland as well as the Republic, in a spirit of mutual co-operation and assistance.

To mark of centenary of the Association, we thought it would be fitting to produce a history of the industry, particularly as there was abundant material and records of all kinds to be drawn from, and as such work had not before been attempted in this country. The passage of time wreaks its ravages on the written word and on the artefacts and industrial archaeology which still survive. Thus the opportunity to record these is timely.

We were fortunate in our choice of author. Charles O'Sullivan, a professional historian, has tackled a task of Herculean proportions, in both its historical and geographical dimensions. The resulting work, we believe, will be of interest to those connected with the industry today, as well as the casual reader with a curiosity about times past in this island. The author adopted a wide canvas as the history of gas in Ireland is closely interwoven with general history, with the great political events as well as the evolution of living and lifestyles over the past century and a half. We are confident that with the changeover to new natural gas, a new chapter is beginning, presaging developments equally extensive and diversified. Future historians will certainly benefit from this pioneering essay into 'the story so far' of the Irish gas industry, the people who worked in it, and the people whom it served.

Nevin Dowling
President, Irish Gas Association

Preface

In a sense, historians can be compared with atomic physicists tracing the minute paths left by sub-atomic particles on sensitive photographic plates, as both are primarily concerned with the examination of noteworthy collisions and exclude, in their considerations, non-contributive or irrelevant elements of past life in the interests of comprehension and lucidity. Whatever the validity of this curious comparison, the gas industry, manufacturing or otherwise, has been one of the discarded and silent factors in Irish economic, social, and political history.[1] Little has been published on the subject in depth and even less in breadth,[2] and what has been published has not always been accurate. The reasons for such neglect range from the preoccupation of Irish historians with more colourful or significant issues to the natural reluctance of gas companies to surrender material which might lead to the excavation, examination, and exposure of embarrassing skeletons.[3] In any case, it has to be admitted that historians predominantly trained in the arts departments of universities have little or no exposure to science or engineering and probably as much love of commerce and industry. It must also be conceded that, until recently, the gas industry played a very minor role in the overall development of a primarily agricultural country as it consisted, for the most part, of numerous small gas-works largely dependent on imports of coal. Indeed, the fact that the industry was relatively small was amply reflected in the relative neglect of gas production in an excellent paper on energy presented to the Royal Dublin Society in 1981 by Richard Kavanagh of the National Board for Science and Technology.[4]

The following thematic sketch is based primarily on sensational newspaper accounts, synoptic journal reports, prejudicial company, corporation and association minutes, unreliable commercial directories, fleeting memories and some exceptional memoirs. It does not feign to be a comprehensive or authoritative study of the Irish gas industry from a technological viewpoint. Neither does it attempt to pass as a sharp economic analysis of the impact of the industry on Irish society, since a considerable amount of material related to the industry has been lost through past indifference, and more has been left untouched by this author in the interests of time and space. Rather, this book pays tribute to the centenary, in 1987, of the North of Ireland Association of Gas Managers, founded in 1887, and which by 1900 had become the Irish Association of Gas Managers and by 1947 the Irish Gas Association. An attempt is made here to preserve and knit together much of what others have seen fit to record relating to the production, distribution and sale of gas. The picture that emerges is one of trials and tribulations, some of which were common to the industry elsewhere and others peculiar to Ireland's particular location, composition and heritage. With the almost complete demise of the traditional town gas utilities on the island, it was thought only fitting that the industry's survival and rejuvenation for more than 160 years should be celebrated in this manner.

As Trevor I. Williams has observed in *A History of the British Gas Industry*, there are few industries which so clearly illustrate the consequences of the interplay of political, technological, economic and social factors.[5] The following deals mainly with events before the discovery and exploitation of natural gas in Ireland. Chapter One gives a brief overview of the technological development of the industry through foreign expertise, further details of which may easily be found elsewhere. The second chapter gives an insight into how the old gas manufacturing industry, whether public or private, was perceived in Ireland during the nineteenth century. The third chapter develops these perceptions by giving some indication of what it was like to work in and about the old town gas utilities before conversion to oil gasification. Finally, the fourth chapter touches upon the distinctive development of the Irish gas manufacturing industry as brought about by particular technological, social, political and international events during the late nineteenth and early twentieth centuries. In coming to write this brief social history, this author has been struck on several occasions by the fact that only those who oppose, abuse, modify, or defend a system of operations are remembered, and freely admits that some of the more colourful material contained herein can hardly be thought typical of the industry as a whole. There is, after all, no denying the essence of Edmund Burke's off-hand remark that half a dozen grasshoppers chatting under a fern should not be considered the only inhabitants of a field simply because they make it chink.[6] Thus, in making some generalisations based upon what might be considered 'the abnormal and peculiar', the present writer chooses to hide behind the conviction that most historical exercises are governed both by the nature of the material available and the prejudices and ability of the reader in question. In any event, there is little point in apologising for either, as something worthy of consideration is surely better than nothing, and can be developed.

With reference to the writing of commerical histories, R.F. Delderfield has suggested that those immediately involved in the day-to-day affairs of business should take the time to write their own story, as simple but sometimes significant entries into ledgers go undetected by 'hired hacks' with an eye to financial gain, especially when they are 'half-way through their chore'.[7] It is inevitable that 'significant' local events, dates and people should be relatively ignored in a general history which hopes to highlight some at the expense of others, and has no ambition to almost endlessly repeat itself through giving a garbled rendering of one company's history after another, in quick succession, to the complete satisfaction of none. No attempt, for instance, is made here to chart the founding dates of the numerous gasworks, to list the relevant directors, managers or secretaries of each, or to tabulate occasional repairs, renewals and constructions. Certainly, the following treatment of the 'gasmakers' might have been richer if gas enthusiasts, formerly within the industry, had been less confined – by the ever-demanding present concerns and all-pervasive futuristic preoccu- pations of business – and written of their experiences in greater detail. Nevertheless, the following impressions are nonetheless interesting, and largely the product of substantial support from both the old and new sectors of the gas industry in Ireland.

In this respect, I wish to thank Declan O'Connell (Irish Gas) who, with the help of Michelle Lloyd, orchestrated accommodation and travelling arrangements after planning the project with Liam Ó hAlmhain and Leslie Allen. Declan promoted the idea as far back as 1983 and gained some interesting information by means of a public appeal in the national press and also by some primary research. He proved an invaluable ally in times of sparcity and occasional impatience. Likewise, I would like to acknowledge the assistance and encouragement of Michael J. Boyle. Liam Ó hAlmhain and Pam MacSwiggan were good enough to allow me parking space in the offices at Dublin Gas, sometimes at ungodly hours, to peruse material they had preserved, while Leslie Allen gladly surrendered valuable material which he had compiled, and even shepherded me through the green pastures of printed bi-annual reports with the collaboration of the Company Secretary! Buoyant good humour and obvious enthusiasm, tempered with a certain curiosity, were the keynotes of relations with all four parties.

Neither, as will become obvious, would this book have been possible without the generous co-operation of Dave Burke, Michael Murphy, Ann Kingston and Bertie Barry at Cork Gas, Jim Keating at Clonmel Gas, Seán

Moran at Limerick Gas, Liam Morgan at Dundalk Gas, John Rice at Wexford Gas and Dennis Enright at Newry Gas. Much credit is also due to various librarians throughout the country – especially in Cork, Limerick, Navan, Dundalk, and Dublin – and to curators of museums in Limerick, Cork, Newry and Clonmel. A special note of thanks is due to Kieran Burke (Cork), Dr Christopher O'Mahony (Limerick), Trevor Parkhill (Belfast PRO) and Brian Donnelly (Dublin PRO) for going beyond the call of duty, and to the overworked staff of the National Library, Dublin. Interviews with Jack Kneeshaw (Clonmel), Jim Cantwell (Wexford), Bill Walsh (Kilkenny), Charlie Copas (Dundalk), David Scott (Dalkey), Leslie Channon (Dundalk) and Joe O'Regan (Waterford), highlighted the danger of losing fleeting memories in the face of technological progress. A lively chat with Councillor Thomas McGrath (Newry) proved interesting, as did material given by Ronnie Buchannan (Dublin Gas), Charles Mollan (Royal Dublin Society), R.S. Anderson and Bill Roberts (Belfast Gas), and Brian Rothery and Teresa McNulty (Institute for Industrial Research and Standards, Dublin). Other sources of information, unfortunately, are too numerous to record.

The Irish Gas Board (Bord Gáis Éireann) was good enough to sponsor the project while the Irish Gas Association provided additional financial support. Friends and parents proved patient as usual. Finally, I would not have written this book without the encouragement and confidence of Professor J.J. Lee, University College Cork.

Chapter 1

International Roots and Early Technology– Gas from Coal

On 23 December 1740, Dr John Clayton, Bishop of Cork, sent the notes of his father's (Reverend John Clayton DD) investigations into the nature of gas to the Earl of Egmont, Sir John Percival, Fellow of the Royal Society. Thus Reverend Clayton became recognised as the first to record the fact that the distillation of coal produced an illuminating gas that could be collected and stored for future use.[1] More than fifty years before, Clayton, who subsequently became Dean of Kildare, had distilled coal in a retort or closed vessel placed in an open fire, collected the resultant gas in bladders, and amused his dinner guests by lighting the gas as it escaped.[2] His experiments had begun around 1684 when he learned that water near Wigan, in Lancashire, had been observed to burn like brandy and even boil eggs and beef to the astonishment of strangers. There, like Thomas Shirley in 1659, he realised that gas, not liquid, was in question. However, he went a step further than Shirley when he associated the gas with coal rather than with the water.[3] It was this vital observation which led him to the distillation of coal and the resultant imprisonment and manipulation of coal gas.

Though perhaps the first to elucidate the basic principles of gas production, John Clayton was but one of many to consider the subject in Europe during the seventeenth and eighteenth centuries. As early as 1609 a Flemish scientist, Jan Baptisa van Helmont, had discovered that 'a wild spirit' escaped from heated coal and wood.[4] Nine years later Jean Tardin thought that the burning flame of gas at Grenoble was similar to that of burning oil or coal.[5] Indeed, by 1681 a professor from Munich, Johann Becker, had discovered that combustible gases resulted from heating coal in the absence of air.[6] Furthermore, in 1727 Englishman Stephen Hales, while ignorant of either Becker or Clayton's observations, discovered that coal gave off an inflammable air on being heated in a closed vessel.[7] About the same time James Lowther piped methane from a mine near Whitehaven, in

Cumbria, to use as an illuminant.[8] In 1730 his agent, Carlisle Spedding, offering to light Whitehaven with gas supplied by means of underground pipes, only to have the idea scotched by local prejudice.[9] In 1760, George Dixon heated coal in a kettle and lit the gas at the end of a pipe attached to the spout, but abandoned any further experiments after an explosion in his pilot plant.[10] Around 1782 Richard Watson, a Cambridge don, conducted experiments related to the weights of different quantities of coal and the relative yield of gas.[11] In 1784 Jan Minckelers distilled powdered coal in a gun barrel to supply balloons, and adopted gas illumination in his lecture theatre in Louvain.[12] In 1785 Professor J.G. Pichel lit his laboratory at Wurzburg with gas.[13] During the early 1780s Archibald Cochrane, the ninth Earl of Dundonald, built ovens to obtain tar for caulking ships from the destructive distillation of coal and used the resultant gas to light his house, Culross Abbey, in Fife.[14] W.A. Lampadius used gas to light the Dresden castle of, the Elector of Saxony in 1799.[15] Meanwhile, the distinguished scientists Robert Boyle, John Mayow, Joseph Priestley, Henry Cavendish, Antoine Lavoissier, François Chaussier and Karl Scheele each worked on the production, isolation, captivation and identification of gases.[16] Clearly, these few examples suggest that the age of gas illumination had finally dawned in Europe by the eighteenth century, even if the gas manufacturing industry had yet to be born there with the able assistance of such men as William Murdock, Philippe Lebon and Frederick Winsor.

William Murdock, the first to study gasmaking from various types of coal under different conditions, became resident agent for the Boulton and Watt mining firm in Cornwall. There he was responsible for the erection and maintenance of mine engines and, as the mines were some miles distant from where he lived, he soon began using bladders full of coal gas, in much the same manner as Clayton, in order to light his way home and shock the locals who associated such practice with the magical arts. In 1792 he used coal gas to light his residence at Redruth and, influenced by Lord Dundonald's work on the distillation of coal in Fife, made the production of gas, rather than that of coke, tar and pitch, the object of his experiments between 1794 and 1795. Three years later, after persuading Boulton and Watt that gas illumination had a promising future, he installed it experimentally in the Soho iron foundry in Birmingham.

At this time, the cotton industry was being revolutionised through the influences of Sir Richard Arkwright, James Hargreaves and Samuel Crompton, with oil lighting being regarded as both dangerous and costly in large, dark establishments, and so the firm of Boulton and Watt set about tapping into this market through gas production. In 1802 a public demonstration was given at Soho to celebrate the temporary Peace of Amiens with Napoleon. This was followed by the permanent installation of

14

gas lighting in the Soho foundry and further experiments costing about £5,000 under the guidance of W. Murdock and S. Clegg, his assistant. In 1805 the cotton mills of Messrs Phillips & Lee at Salford, Manchester, adopted gas lighting under the direction of Murdock as did Henry Lodge's cotton mill at Sowerby Bridge under Samuel Clegg. Naturally, opinions varied as to who was first to make gas illumination a commercial venture, but William Murdock was awarded the Rumford Gold Medal by the Royal Society for his efforts, in 1808.

Others were not as fortunate as Murdock in their attempts to promote the commercial use of gas. In France, for instance, Philippe Lebon produced gas from sawdust, patented 'a new method of employing combustible materials more effectively either for heating or lighting' in 1799, and held public demonstrations in Paris, using two *thermolampes*, in 1801. However, in pre-industrial France Lebon failed to win immediate or widespread local support with the general attitude to such innovation amply reflected by Rothschild's observation to the effect that investments in women, gambling and engineers were three sure ways of losing money with the first two being infinitely more pleasant and the last being definitely more certain![17] Nevertheless, Lebon's efforts were not wasted in that he did influence others, before his assassination on the Champs Élysées in 1804. Among these were Zachaus Winzler, a Moravian chemical manufacturer, who promoted gas cooking as early as 1802, and Friedrich Albrecht Winzler, a German professor of commerce, who abandoned efforts to promote gas lighting on the Continent and went to London in 1803. There he changed his name to Frederick Winsor, patented a gas lighting system and launched a vigorous and determined publicity campaign to promote it. His aim was to set up Britain's first gas company.

Frederick Winsor realised that the future of gas illumination lay not in private generation plants, as promoted by Boulton and Watt for instance, but in a centralised generative and distributive network. In claiming that gas would alleviate asthma and pulmonary troubles, reduce the plight of unhappy chimney boys and offer enormous profits to courageous speculators, he naturally met with opposition, vested or otherwise. Sir Walter Scott, for instance, ridiculed the mad notion of lighting London with smoke![18] He was not alone in dismissing Winsor's scheme. W.H. Wollaston believed that London could just as easily be lit with a slice from the moon, while Sir Humphry Davy considered the suitability of the dome of St Paul's as a gasholder![19] Others earnestly argued that the replacement of oil by gas would undermine national defence, since the whaling fleet served as a reliable source of recruits for the Royal Navy during an emergency. Initial efforts to convince the Chancellor of the Exchequer, the Privy Council and King George III of the benefits of gas all failed, so that only in 1810 did the new company acquire legal rights to lay the necessary mains and pipes. Then, in 1812, the required financial conditions of its charter were achieved with the Gas Light and Coke Company coming formally into existence, to be followed by others in London, Edinburgh, Glasgow, Liverpool, Bristol, Bath, Cheltenham, Birmingham, Leeds, Manchester, Exeter, Chester and Bath by 1819. Clearly, Winsor's contagious enthusiasm for the idea of centralised gas production had put the industry on a steady footing.

PURIFICATION

A major problem in the early production of gas was purification, but by 1819 this was no longer so. In 1806 Edward Heard had discovered that lime helped to remove some of the poisonous hydrogen sulphide and other sulphur impurities found in coal gas and had obtained a patent for the purification of gas with dry lime, which, with exposure to air after use, could easily be sold for agricultural use.[20] In the same year, Samuel Clegg had introduced a more popular method – wet liming – whereby a bucketful of lime suspended in about fifty gallons of water would purify about 20,000 cubic feet of gas bubbling through it. John Malam then devised a compact triple purifier on this principle, before improving upon Reuben Phillips's

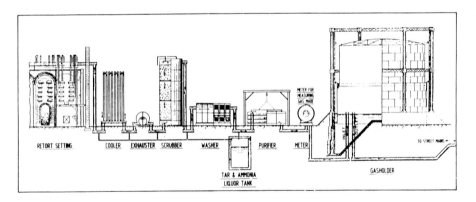

The principle of making gas from coal remained the same through the years and the above is a simplified section, from left to right, showing the production process.

The process began at the fire-clay retort where coal was fired and the gas, given off through combustion, flowed to its first stage of treatment into the condenser (cooler). This cooling gas gave off water vapour and tarry by-products. An exhauster (compressor or form of pump) was used to draw the gas along into the scrubber tower where the gas was washed and further impurities removed. The washer and purifier were continuations of this cleaning process. The gas finally passed through the station meter before entering the gasholder.

A reliable coal-delivering system to Midleton Gas Works in 1953. The condenser, washer, scrubber and purifier may be seen in the background.

1817 process for purifying gas with slack lime. Only by about 1850 was lime for purification superseded somewhat through F.C. Hill's promotion of iron-oxide. This could be used several times over with exposure to air and eventually sold as a weed-killer. In Ireland it was known as '*meather*' and was exported from Westmeath to London as late as the 1950s.

RETORTS

Innovations remained to be made in other aspects of the production process and consequently the technological development of retorts reflected the rapid pace of change within the industry. A retort is defined as a continuous carbonisation vessel of any capacity. In the early part of the nineteenth century retorts were generally horizontal, constructed of steel, and required constant resetting as the extremely high temperatures damaged the retort's structure.

The problem of damage was overcome by the widespread introduction of fire-clay retorts by the 1840s. A further development in this period was the through retort where the by-product of carbonisation coke could be withdrawn from the opposite end to which the coal was added. The process of filling retorts with coal was known as 'charging', and the removal of coke 'discharging'.

By the 1870s automatic charging was in use although hand-charging was in use well into the twentieth century. Gas production in the old horizontal retort was frequently interrupted for recharging as the charging and discharging was not a continuous process. Gravity provided a solution and a Frenchman, André Coze used an inclined retort by 1885. As the retort was set at an angle of 32°, gravitational pull assisted the charging and discharging operation.

By the beginning of the twentieth century vertical retorts were in use and these facilitated non-stop carbonisation. The charging with coal took place through the top of the retort and the discharging of coke through the bottom, facilitated by gravity.

Work done by Thaddeus Lowe and Tessie du Motay in the 1870s in the production of water gas was applied to the vertical retort. The first step was to pass steam through the incandescent coke at a temperature of $1,000^{\circ}$C. to obtain blue water gas (BWG). This BWG consisted mainly of carbon monoxide and hydrogen in almost equal amounts. The quantity of gas produced was increased considerably though the calorific value (CV) was reduced. To obtain gas of a higher CV and, more importantly at the time, to improve its illuminating power the BWG would be mixed with an oil spray and passed through hot refractories (fire-bricks) to produce carburetted water gas (CWG).

The Belfast vertical gas retort house, circa 1913

By the end of 1893 Belfast, for instance, had a CWG plant in operation (see diagram) alongside their coal gas plant. It was judged in a contemporary account to be 'remarkable alike for its great simplicity and its large efficiency'. The following is a description of the water gas plant by engineer and manager James Stelfox in 1896.

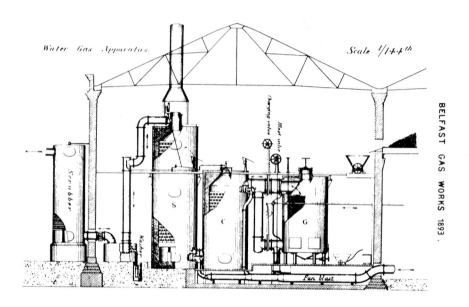

Into the first vessel G, known as the generator, coke is piled to a working depth of 6 to 7 feet, and being ignited is brought to a high temperature by means of a powerful blast. The products, consisting of carbonic oxide and carbonic acid in varying proportions, together with the nitrogen of the air, pass into the second vessel C, known as the carburetter. At the entrance to this vessel, secondary air is admitted, which effects the partial or complete combustion, as may be desired, of the carbonic oxide into carbonic acid. The resultant gases pass on into the superheater S, at the entrance to which secondary air is again available, in order that complete combustion of the carbonic oxide may be effected here, if it has not already been accomplished in the carburetter. The final products escape into the atmosphere by means of the stack valve, which is left open. This portion of the process is known as 'blowing', and its object is to get up the heat, firstly in the generator, so as to secure the breaking up of the steam in the succeeding operation of gas-making or 'running', and secondly in the carburetter and superheater, so as to effect the proper 'cracking' or gasification of the oil. These two vessels are filled with chequer work of fire-bricks so laid as to baffle the gases in their progress; the spaces left between the bricks are about 2 inches wide. By the spent heat of the generator and the combustion of the carbonic oxide this brickwork becomes heated; and when the temperature reaches about 1,700° Fahr. gas-making or "running" may commence. For this purpose the blast is now shut off, steam of about 100 lbs. pressure is turned on into the generator, and the stack valve is closed down. The steam follows the same course as the blast, and in its passage through the hot coke it gives up its oxygen to form carbonic oxide, whereby the hydroen is liberated; and there is thus delivered into the carburetter a gas consisting theoretically of equal volumes of carbonic oxide and hydrogen, which has no illuminating value, but a high heating power. On its entrance into the carburetter, a douche of petroleum oil is sprayed upon hot iron bars placed over the brick chequer work. This oil is preferably heated beforehand by being passed through a delivery pipe which is carried through the main outlet of hot gas. It is at once vaporized and picked up by the non-illuminating water-gas; and in its passage the mixture comes in contact with the hot chequer work, whereby the complete 'cracking' or gasification of the oil is effected, which is the sole purpose of the carburetter and superheater. Passing through the main outlet, which is sealed in water so as to prevent any return of the gas, the carburetted water-gas is led on into the ordinary cooling and purifying apparatus, to be there treated in the same way as ordinary gas. The process of 'running' is necessarily one of cooling also; and if it were continued too long, the coke in the generator would become too cool to break up the steam, and the surface of the brick chequer work would grow too cold to effect the 'cracking' of the oil. Therefore when gas-making has gone on for about seven minutes, the steam is shut off, the stack valve opened, and blowing is resumed for about four minutes, by which time the normal heat in the three vessels is restored, and another spell of 'running' commences. After four 'runs' have been made, the generator requires replenishing with a supply of coke, which can be fed in through the charging hole at top in about half a minute; and about once in every twelve hours it requires clinkering, a warm and unpleasant operation, which however occupies only about a quarter to half an hour.[21]

GASHOLDERS

Improvements were also made with regard to storage. Public safety in the vicinity of gasholders was a continuing cause for concern, and Winsor preferred to discharge any excess gas into the air irrespective of cost. In 1813 a deputation from the Royal Society recommended that holders should not exceed a capacity of 6,000 cubic feet and should be protected by an independent structure, before Samuel Clegg demonstrated to them the safety of gasholders by striking one with an axe and lighting the gas as it

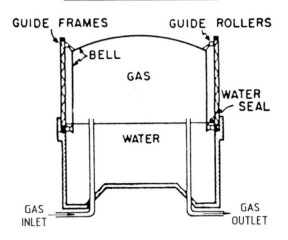

GAS HOLDER
WET SEAL TYPE
– NON TELESCOPIC VERSION

GUIDE FRAMES   GUIDE ROLLERS

BELL

GAS

WATER
SEAL

WATER

GAS
INLET

GAS
OUTLET

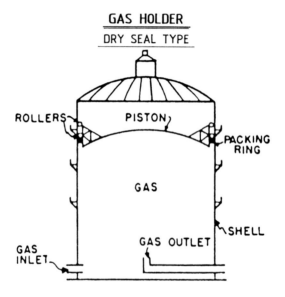

GAS HOLDER
DRY SEAL TYPE

ROLLERS   PISTON

PACKING
RING

GAS

SHELL

GAS
INLET

GAS OUTLET

Gasholders, also known as gasometers, evolved into a number of different types – though the original principle, of a vessel in which gas was stored and in which compensation could be made for fluctuations in the rate of gas production and demand, remained the same. The illustration shows two basic types of gasholder – the wet-seal and the dry-seal types – both of which were common in Ireland.

escaped without causing an explosion. At the time gasholders were mainly and simply cylindrical in shape with water at their base. An inverted bell contained the gas, and the base of this bell rested in the water to prevent the gas escaping. The bell was raised or dropped according as the amount of gas rose or fell.

Early trials with different types of gasholder in adverse environments were carried out by Clegg and, while these were not successful, his work led to the invention of the wet-meter.[22] However, in 1824 the water-sealed telescopic holder was produced in which the cylindrical portion of the bell was formed of more than one section or lift and, as the gasholder emptied, the sections telescoped into each other.

Further modifications were made by the late 1880s when weighted wire cables to guide the movement of the holder replaced the large surrounding framework. By then waterless gasholders had been devised, by which the gas was contained beneath a movable piston with a tar seal around the edges, so that problems related to frost, effluent disposal and pipe corrosion from within were reduced. Allowing easy regulation of pressure and dispensing with the need for expensive foundations, these gasholders became permanent fixtures in many townscapes during the twentieth century.

METERS

Like the early gasholders, the wet-meters designed by Samuel Clegg in 1815 and John Malam in 1819 were naturally subject to environmental conditions affecting water. Accordingly, they were eventually superseded, in domestic supply, by dry-meters devised by Miles Barry in 1833 and Alexander Wright in 1844, before the patenting of the pre-payment meter by T.S. Lacey in 1870 and the introduction of the slot meter in 1887. Meters spelt the welcome revision of the old untrustworthy system whereby company–consumer relations were governed more by the time permitted for consumption than by the volume of gas consumed.[23] This arrangement had required inspectors to enforce regulations limiting the supply of gas at certain hours, retarded to some degree the application of gas for cooking, and expected customers to pay in accordance with a pre-ordained rate related to the hours of supply requested and the type and number of burners used.

BURNERS

Burners, too, changed and developed. In the early days, the most common burners for lighting were Clegg's burner of 1809, Stone's batwing burner of 1816, and the union jet invented by James Neilson and James Milne in 1820. The union jet, or fish-tail burner, contained two holes

The spiral guided gasholder in Belfast Gasworks, built just before the First World War, which had a capacity of just over 1½ million cubic feet. In the foreground is an empty smaller spiral gasholder, built twenty years previously, with a capacity of 76,000 cubic feet

Gasholders at Cork Gas. In the foreground is an empty vertical guided water-sealed gasholder which had a capacity of 350,000 cubic feet. The background is dominated by a spiral guided water-sealed gasholder with a capacity of 500,000 cubic feet.

inclined at an angle to allow the resultant twin gas streams to coalesce and produce a flat flame which was more rigid and independent of draughts than that produced by the batwing burner with its dome-shaped top and single slit. In both cases, however, the amount of light produced depended to a large extent on whether or not the gas was produced from expensive cannel coal. The light emitted was poor in most instances, despite the numerous variations devised, until the principle of drawing air into the flame – as involved in the argand oil burner – was applied to gasburners during the mid-nineteenth century. One such lamp was W. Sugg's argand burner which was adopted as the parliamentary standard burner in legislation related to the testing of the quality of gas in 1868. This was modified by Robert Bunsen in 1853 and only superseded by the flat flame burner, for gas fires, during the 1930s. Indeed, use of the Bunsen burner by the Austrian chemist, Carl Auer von Welsbach, led to the discovery of the incandescent mantle in 1884 which helped to ward off competition from electricity well into the twentieth century. In the case of the Welsbach mantle the luminosity of the gas itself was irrelevant as the light emitted was governed by the extent to which the oxides of the rare earth metals, contained in the mantle, were heated and the highest temperatures produced were those by gas with an almost non-luminous flame. In the gas industry concerns for illumination were soon to be followed by developments in heating and cooking.

COOKING AND HEATING

Philippe Lebon and Zachaus Winzler, as already mentioned, had promoted the use of gas for cooking at the turn of the eighteenth century. With the introduction of meters during the mid-nineteenth century, the forerunner of the modern gas ring in 1867 and the gas oven thermostat in 1923, gas as a medium for cooking went from strength to strength. Methods of heating water also improved with the invention of the geyser by Benjamin Maugham in 1868 (although the early geysers had no flue and were not exactly safe or efficient without further improvements) and the introduction of automatic lighting from a pilot light during the 1930s. Methods of heating air also improved, overcoming the problem of the economical distribution of energy through suitable radiants, with Leoni's successful gas fire in 1882. This particular gas fire provided heat by thermal radiation from a back consisting of fire-brick in which tufts of asbestos were embedded, and used an adaptation of a Bunsen burner to give a hotter flame than had been possible with the earlier heaters of the mid-nineteenth century. It was improved upon during the twentieth century with the introduction of columnar radiants in 1905, the grid form in 1925, the neat-flame during the 1930s, and the convector gasfire during the mid-1950s.

GAS MANUFACTURE

As the use of gas for lighting diminished there was a growth in its use for heating leading to these developments. Likewise, the process of gas manufacture was modernised because of competition from other fuels. Conventional gas production – through the distillation of either bituminous coal, fish-oil or turf – was labour intensive, due to the nature of the raw materials and resultant impurities, and was therefore increasingly expensive. With growing competition from other fuels, diminished markets for profit-making residual products (such as coke, tar and ammonical liquor), mounting costs for coal, transport and storage, and dwindling stocks of good quality coal, the industry recognised the need for more advanced techniques of gas production in the interests of survival. The production of carburetted water-gas, referred to earlier, set the stage for the idea of the elimination of tar and coke residuals and the utilisation of ordinary coal through various processes of complete gasification as devised, with varying success, by William Siemens in 1861, Ludwig Mond in 1889, C.B. Tully in 1918, and Lurgi in the early 1920s. Lurgi's process has been credited with being the first successful one to be carried out,[24] and basically involved the simultaneous occurrence of two chemical reactions to form carbon monoxide, hydrogen, and a little methane. Through combination with steam in the presence of a catalyst at about 800°C. in a process known as the water-gas shift reaction, the carbon monoxide was then converted to carbon dioxide, and this removed by passing the gases through an alkaline solution, so that the hydrogen gas could be purified and enriched as required for sales.

Though relatively successful in Germany with brown coals, this process required modification for British black coals and had a number of shortcomings. For instance, it required tons of expensive oxygen and left large quantities of weak ammonia liquor which required costly treatment before sale. In any event, the Lurgi process did not prove to be competitive with the new oil gasification processes developed in the British Isles after the Second World War. Here, it was discovered that a light distillate (naphtha) – consisting of volatile hydrocarbons obtained as a product of petroleum refining – combined to produce hydrogen, carbon dioxide, carbon monoxide and small quantities of methane when at a pressure of between twenty and thirty atmospheres and at a temperature of between 700° and 900°C. in the presence of a catalyst. As with Lurgi gas, the required enrichment could be achieved through the addition of either butane or propane. Alternatively, it could be secured through the catalytic rich gas process or through subjection to steam reforming in what is called the pre-heat/re-heat process. Indeed, it was also found that there was an alternative oil gasification technique to these processes depending upon the

27

gasification of light petroleum distillate by reaction with super-heated steam in the presence of a catalyst. This involved the marriage of the distillate with hydrogen, at high pressure and temperature, to produce methane and ethane.

In simpler terms, then, the industry underwent a revolution which encouraged it to move away from the traditional methods of pyrolysing coal in retorts. With favourable oil prices, less manpower, less danger, less space, and no solid by-products in need of disposal, gas could be produced from oil at approximately half the costs incurred through coal distillation. However, the positive impact of these technological developments and scientific insights did not materialise overnight, nor appear without their attendant legal, technological, and administrative problems. Indeed, in Britain for instance, 90 percent of the gas produced still came from coal as late as 1960. Accordingly, there is a corresponding temptation to overlook this constructive stage in the light of subsequent fluctuations in regard to oil prices and in the wake of more recent developments pertaining to the application of natural gas for domestic and industrial purposes.

NATURAL GAS

The utilisation of natural gas as distinct from manufactured gas in the western world is a comparatively recent event. The following entry by Ch'ang Ch'u in his 'Records of the Country South of Mount Hua' in 347 B.C. points to a much earlier use in the Orient.

> At the place where the river from Pu-p'u joins the Huo-ching River, there are fire wells; at night the glow is reflected all over the sky. The inhabitants wanted to have fire, and used to ignite the gas outlets with brands from household hearths; after a short time there would be a noise like the rumbling of thunder and the flames would shoot out so brilliantly as to light up the country for several dozen li around [several miles at least]. Moreover they use bamboo tubes to contain the light, conserving it so that it can be made to travel from one place to another, as much as a day's journey away from the well without it being extinguished. When it burns no ash is left, and it blazes brilliantly.[25]

In China, long before the first century B.C., drilling for natural gas followed close on the heels of drilling for brine. Indeed, the relative backwardness of the West in this respect could hardly have been otherwise as Robert K.G. Temple has convincingly argued that Europeans could not have developed deep cable drilling techniques, even if they had wanted to, as they had no material equivalent to bamboo until the mid-nineteenth century:

The bamboo cables were made of strips 40 feet long. A single-strength cable would be used down to 1,500 feet but at depths greater than that the cable was of double thickness. The tensile strength of hemp rope is 750 pounds per square inch whereas that of bamboo is nearly four tons per square inch, equal to some steel wire. The bamboo was also so flexible that it could easily be wound up round the borehead winding drum. Bamboo cables had the added advantage of becoming tougher when wet, the opposite of rope. . . . using hemp ropes as cables for drill bits would have been like drilling with a rubber ball on the end of a piece of elastic.[26]

Apparently, the first news of Chinese drilling techniques in Europe had come by way of Dutch explorers during the seventeenth century. However, the first full description of the process came in the form of correspondence from a French missionary, named Imbert, in 1828. This was discussed by an incredulous French Scientific Society in 1829, and applied to brine drilling by 1834 and oil drilling by 1841. Similarly, in America, Chinese techniques were adopted by 1859, possibly through the influence of Chinese indentured labourers employed in building the railways there during the nineteenth century.

Although gas wells were known to exist in Japan as early as A.D. 615, and China in A.D. 900, and although Western deep drilling may be viewed as an importation from China, the origin of the modern natural gas industry undoubtedly lies in the United States. Here, in 1821, some forty-six years after George Washington described 'a burning spring' on a stretch of land granted to him by General Andrew Lewis in 1775, the first utilisation of gas occurred[27] — some boys playing on the bank of the Canadaway Creek accidently ignited a seepage of gas and thereby encouraged the citizens of Fredonia to drill a well and pipe the gas to nearby residences. Thirty-seven years later the gas was still going strong so the Fredonia Gas Light and Water Works was established to become the world's first natural gas corporation,[28] to join the other 183 town gas utilities in operation, with a view to public and private lighting, at the time.[29] With an eye to heating and industrial functions, the natural gas industry went almost hand in hand with the older US manufacturing industry and progressed with new-found spurts and spasms, and natural stops and starts. Indeed, J.M. Critchlow asserted, in 1885, that natural gas 'could never be a serious menace to the manufacturing gas industry', while Charles Harrison declared, in 1890, that 'natural gas stocks are speculative and have never risen to the dignity of legitimate investment and there is no prospect that they ever will.'[30] However, while some companies suffered short and hectic lives, the overall consumption of natural gas rose from $215,000 in 1882 to $22,629,875 in 1888 and $23,700,000 in 1900. Natural gas was odourised in 1885, sold by the meter in 1891, liquefied by 1940, and piped to markets thousands of miles distant by the 1950s. Clearly, the United States had led the way in regard to the distribution of natural gas as Britain had in regard to the traditional gas manufacturing industry.

IRELAND

Lying between these two industrial giants, Ireland could not but follow them. Indeed, this fact was highlighted by members of the Irish Gas Association as late as 1975 when they noted that British manufacturers of gas appliances were moving away from 'bread and butter appliances', required by the manufacturing industry in Ireland, because the old gas manufacturing industry in Britain was being phased out. By 1977 there was a serious reduction in the number of appliances available and increasing difficulties encountered through deliveries taking up to six months. However, to acknowledge Ireland's former dependence upon Britain is not to suggest that she did not look elsewhere for the fruits of technological endeavour. For instance, Ireland was looking towards improved turf distillation techniques in France, Sweden, Germany and Russia as late as the 1930s and 1950s. As it happens, the first large turf distillation factory in the world, with the object of preparing and purifying turf-tar and gas-water, was founded in 1849 at Kilberry near Athy on the results of experiments performed by a Mr Reece in Paris and in Newtown Cromelin, Co. Armagh.[31] Indeed, there were three gasworks in Dublin in 1824, one operating from coal, one from fish-oil and another from turf.[32] The utilisation of foreign coal, however, proved most profitable prior to oil gasification and conversion to natural gas, and thereby made the traditional gas industry a victim, rather than master, of international developments.

Chapter Two

Public Lighting and Controversy

The welcome discovery of natural gas off the Old Head of Kinsale in 1971 led to the establishment of Bord Gáis Éireann Teoranta in 1975 – formally set up in 1976 under the Gas Act as Bord Gáis Éireann, the Irish Gas Board. Since then admirable progress has been made in developing and promoting the use of gas for heating and in industry and agriculture. Earlier use of gas, however, was confined largely to lighting.

In Ireland, as elsewhere, gas glowly displaced candle and oil power for public lighting in numerous urban areas during the nineteenth century and effectively competed with electric lighting well into the twentieth century. At the early stages of its development the Irish gas industry benefitted from the protection, prestige, promotion and profits associated with the manufacture of gas for public lighting in Britain. Closely in step with British, French and American developments, Ireland was well in advance of similar efforts at public lighting by gas in Germany, Sweden, Switzerland, Italy, Spain, Denmark, Poland, Malta, Austria, Canada, and Japan,[1] containing as many as four gasworks in 1822, twenty-eight in 1846, forty-three in 1856, and 114 in 1881.[2]

The advantages of gas were obvious, as suggested by a 'Gas Prospectus for Londonderry' in 1822. Relative to candle and oil power, it was cheap, clean, safe and brilliant.[3] Oil lamps were almost unbearably expensive to maintain. In Cork in 1717, for instance, a fellow called Peter Dane was paid as much as four to five shillings for 'each dark of the moon' in which he attended four oil lamps.[4] Indeed, in 1772, after an unsatisfactory legal discussion on the Red House Walk (now the Mardyke), the respectable citizens of Cork enthusiastically resorted to the novel but drastic method of smashing all the public lamps in order to rid themselves of the hated lamp tax.[5] It was but a temporary solution, as public lamps, no matter how poor in quality or excessive in cost, were better than nothing, especially in Cork

Gas lamps, Belfast 1870.

with its naked quays and littered streets![6] A nasty fall from a horse might not be survived because of the practice of medicinal bleeding and only the wealthier citizens could afford to employ link-boys with lanterns to chart their way about dark, dirty, and dangerous streets. Burglaries were common and the poorly-lit alleys winked at theft and violence.

In Dublin in 1819 even hall-door rappers and brass labels were not safe from the prowling set of vagabonds who committed 'nightly deprivations . . . almost under the eye of the watchful guardian, on each corner, and in each street'.[7] A favourite practice among Dublin thieves was to snare a solitary stranger by leaving a loop of chord on the pavement and then jerking it when he put his foot in it.[8] Darkness tolerated destruction, human or otherwise, and, as one observer moaned, some thirty beautiful young trees would not have been ravaged in Mitchelstown, Co. Cork, in 1901 had it possessed gas lighting.[9]

EARLY PUBLIC LIGHTING

Gas was first used for public lighting in Ireland some fifteen years after Frederick Winsor demonstrated his idea of distributing gas through underground pipes connected to a central gasworks in London in 1808. A display of gas lighting in Belfast on 30 August 1823 drew a large crowd who 'were highly gratified by the mild radiance flowing from the lamps'.[10] However, the idea of gas illumination was by no means new on the island, with a private gas plant in Cork, for instance, as early as 1816[11] and as many as two competing gas companies in Dublin in 1823.

Dubliners had not been slow to realise the advantages of gas lighting. Even though a Mr Grattan, Mr Shaw and 'numerous others, equally respectable as to rank, talent, and integrity'[12] had objected to the notion of underground pipes for public and private lighting on grounds of noxious vapours and water contamination in 1819, with the clarification of legal rights and duties, only the existence of a corrupt Paving and Lighting Board had prevented the introduction of gas lighting until 1824. And by then the citizens of Dublin were familiar with it. Crowe Street Theatre, for instance, had installed a private gas plant (at a cost of £1,800) as early as 1818.[13]

Indeed, there was sharp competition between the Dublin Coal Gas Light Company for Ireland of Great Brunswick Street in 1822. In that year the Oil Gas Company highlighted the use of gas in the General Post Office and in the public press, in order to celebrate and differentiate 'the newly invented and improved gas from oil, as patented by our highly spirited and much esteemed countryman, Alderman West', from that produced from coal.

Patrick Street, Cork, in the nineteenth century when street gas lighting 'made the darkness visible'.

Oil Gas . . . requires no purification, nor does it contain any sulphurous hydrogen, which is considered so obnoxious to health, and which acts so powerfully on metals as in the course of time to injure the fittings, pipes, etc., through which it passes.[14]

The production of oil gas could be considered 'as an undertaking calculated to promote, to a great extent, the revival of the Fisheries, the nursery for our seamen.'[15] This nationalistic statement from *The Freeman's Journal* is all the more interesting with the realisation that the Patent Oil Gas Light Company was as British as its competitor, the Coal Gas Company, having been founded, like similar works in Bristol, Edinburgh, Hull and Liverpool, after Messrs Gosling and Taylor had failed to secure legal rights to provide London with oil gas.

LONDON MONOPOLIES AND NATIVE COMPETITION

Such nationalistic sentiments were to prove common with the foundation of new and competing gasworks in Dublin and elsewhere. The Hibernian Gas Light Company, floated in Dublin in 1823, is an interesting example, as voiced by *The Freeman's Journal* of 17 October 1826:

The professed objects of the Company were to light the city of Dublin and its suburbs with Gas, and the necessary works were commenced with vigour and all the usual machinery put in motion. The eventful year of 1824 now commenced, and all the artillery of the speculators was brought forward to push this New National Gas Company into notice. – The celebrated name of 'Daniel O'Connell' was inserted in the Act and Prospectus, as a Director, obviously 'ad captandum', and thus to take the Irish public by a ruse, as the world must have known that Daniel had enough to do to regulate his own Gasometer, and supply the necessary quantity of his inflammable air to all denominations of his Irish people without devoting his precious time to the multifarious arrangements of a Joint Stock Company – however, it had its effects.

Although the prospectus of the Hibernian Gas Light Company had set forth the great profits derived from similar companies in London, the response in Ireland to the floating of shares in 1823 had hardly been enthusiastic owing to the depressed state of the stock of the older Dublin Coal Gas Light Company. Nevertheless, through the exertions of an English insurance agent called Davy, the subscribed capital of £50,000 was paid and certificates granted to provide Dublin with a third gas company.

Meanwhile, the ordinary citizens of Dublin took gas lighting to their hearts, and the relevant commissioners to task. On Tuesday, 3 August 1824 a public meeting was held at the Royal Exchange and chaired by the Lord

Mayor, in order to air grievances and formulate a petition 'to his Excellency the Lord Lieutenant' so that 'he will be pleased speedily to adopt such measures as will procure for the City of Dublin such accommodation in regard to its lighting as may be suitable to its role among the cities of the Empire.' Here, it was unanimously resolved

> that the experience of the past fifteen years has proved . . . that the Establishment for Paving and Lighting this City is burdensome, inefficient, and unsatisfactory. That the power of taxation with which the Commissioners are entrusted, by the Act of 1817, have not been exercised with due discretion, in as much as these Commissioners have invariably enforced the maximum thereof, whereby they have been enabled at all times to have the command of many thousands . . . beyond the sum applied to the purposes of the establishment, and without having afforded the necessary accommodation which the citizens had a right to suspect for the actual expenditure.[16]

The grievances were real. In Lower Mount Street in 1819, for instance, there were frequent accidents through people failing to see that stoppers had been stolen from coal vaults.[17] Newspaper accounts suggest that lighting was but a casual affair. Why else would one citizen, making a tour from the neighbourhood of Thomas Street to Stephen's Green and back between the hours of three and four on the 23 February 1819, go to the bother of noting that only three lamps were lighting in Cornmarket, one in Blacklane, two in Bride Alley, two in Bride Street, none in Peter Street, three in Aungier Street, one in York Street, one in Little Longford Street, two in Golden Lane, none in Chancery Lane, two in Kennedy Lane and two in High Street?[18] Poor lighting, coupled with irregular pavements, guaranteed regular accidents at all hours. John Williams Esq., for instance, one of Her Majesty's Counsel, fell from a horse 'owing to the extreme darkness of the night, and no lamps being lit (although between seven and eight-o-clock)', combined with the problem of an extremely high footpath.[19] Indeed, one street in the vicinity of Trinity College was considered so bad that it was suggested that 'the surgeons . . . remove their Hall from Stephen's Green to this break-neck avenue' so as to be able to render immediate assistance 'to the maimed and wounded'![20]

THE DARKNESS MADE VISIBLE – AND OTHER COMPLAINTS

On 16 August 1824 *The Freeman's Journal* gladly announced that

> by the conduct of the Paving Commissioners, their powers, as to lighting the City are defunct, the Lord Lieutenant having caused Contracts to be entered

into with the Dublin Gas Companies, without the control of the Paving Board whose conduct the last nine years in refusing all Contracts for Gas, appeared inexplicable and might have remained so had not the Citizens come forward and called on our Chief Magistrate . . .

The decision of the Lord Lieutenant to bypass the paving commissioners was not altogether surprising given that he had seen the need to contract for five thousand link-boys before holding 'a drawing room' on 29 December 1823.[21] It was foolish then not to utilise the presence of three competing gas companies, all legally obliged to light the streets in which they had mains and at prices not in excess of those charged in London.

Once established, gas was a less expensive, more convenient and more effective medium than oil in dispersing darkness. That is not to suggest, however, that all complaints about public and private lighting in Dublin ceased with the introduction of gas. In February 1826, for instance, *The Dublin Evening Post* declared:

> The Gas Lamps from the corner of Grafton Street to Kildare Street were completely extinguished at an early hour on Monday night last. The storm of that night might furnish an excuse for the occurrence were it not that all the respectable inhabitants of that quarter have so many complaints of its frequency, and it is to be found in all the Police Reports of Dublin that some neglect is attributable to the Company or those to whom the duty of inspecting on this subject has been deputed.

Complaints continued to flow forth regarding the cost, quality and duration of gas lighting. While it was long held that oil hardly made darkness visible,[22] it was later grudgingly conceded that Dublin gas possessed the ability only to do so.[23] It was even claimed, in 1865, that the best place for an offender to hide in Dublin was under a gas lamp![24]

As always, townsmen were slow to part with hard-earned cash to promote public safety or bolster private profit, but were quick to question local conditions within the Irish and British context. This was clearly evident in 1844 when Dublin citizens followed the example of Limerick and Manchester in demanding a corporation gasworks which would dissipate profits for the common good.[25] Dublin gas prices were compared with those of Belfast, Wexford, Derry, Limerick, and Liverpool in 1844, and those of Edinburgh, Belfast and Cork in 1865.[26] The fact that other conditions varied did not always count for much in public estimation.

Having realised that there was a certain degree of financial security in gas production, and no real secret involved in the same, the rising middle classes in urban Ireland naturally opposed foreign monopolies and eagerly favoured reduced prices and shared profits. Even outside Dublin concrete consumer

complaints were sometimes supported by energetic economic enterprise —
both Limerick and Clonmel contained two competing gasworks in 1842, as
did Carlow in 1847, Cork in 1857, Newtownards in 1870, Lisburn,
Cookstown, Downpatrick and Naas in 1881, and Waterford in 1897. Such
bold ventures were led, won and directed by socially and nationally
conscious men like Charles Bianconi, Daniel O'Connell, John Francis
Maguire and Sir John Grey. The concern was not purely economic as the
founding of a new company did not bring quick profit or immediate success.
The second gas company in Limerick, managed by the corporation, did not
produce dividends for years while the new Cork Consumer's Company
charged higher and healthier prices in the gas war than the old British-based
concern.[27] Nevertheless, both gasworks survived and won because Cork
and Limerick, like Clonmel, could afford to welcome British expertise
while rejecting British ownership. Others, like Ennis,[28] were not so
fortunate, having little choice but to wait until the introduction of electricity
to rid themselves of exorbitant gas charges. Others, like Macroom, were
either too poor, mean or badly situated to support even one gasworks.

DUBLIN 1824–1845: THE BREAKING OF MONOPOLY

Competing gas companies did not always benefit Irish society. In Dublin
between 1824 and 1826 three gas companies operated in competition with
one another until they realised that neighbouring and competing gasworks
benefitted the consumer rather than the companies. Thus, having originally
followed the practice of sharing streets and the multiple laying of mains in
the interests of consumer prejudice (and the habitual thieving of gas from
nearby pipes in the name of company profit and sport), the rival gas
companies decided to divide the city into areas and agreed to limit their
separate operations to specified districts. As *The Freeman's Journal* commented in 1826, 'a monopoly to each was created and the general interests of
the citizens sacrificed to the individual interests of the parties concerned.'
Moreover, by 1826 the parties concerned were mainly British, as the native
Hibernian Gas Company had been taken over by the London-based United
General Gas Company, at a cost of £22 premium on each share, after it had
secured the contract for the entire or exclusive public lighting of Dublin.
Thus, it was calculated in 1826 that as much as £30,000 per annum would go
to London from 'this impoverished city' in return for good light.[29]
Discontent was predictable and took positive shape within eighteen years
when a group of prominent citizens formed the Dublin Consumers' Gas
Company in opposition to the United General Gas Company which, with
the expenditure of £300,000,[30] had acquired the shares of the three gas
companies legally entitled to light the city.

In 1844 discontent with gas conditions crystallised around the issue of the Hibernian's (United General's) performance in the matter of public lighting because its contract, which had lasted for nineteen years, needed to be renewed in that year. Rivalry between the new corporation and the old paving board was also central to the issue as was the fact that the initial and vigorous competition between the United General and Alliance (founded in 1835) gas companies of the mid- and late-thirties had evaporated in the interests of mutual survival and increased profits.[31] At a meeting of the corporation in August, Councillor Kirwan referred to the high-handed manner in which the paving board had negotiated with the Hibernian Gas Company while keeping interested parties and public representatives in the dark. He asserted that the proposed renewal of contract was an absolute bargain to the gas company and asked what cities within the empire paid more than Dublin.[32] He pointed to the fact that profits from the manufacture of gas in Manchester, ranging from £30,000 to £40,000 per annum, went towards the payment of municipal rates. To some, this line of argument seemed unreasonable, with Dublin possessing two gas companies and only one (the Hibernian/United General) entitled or willing to contract for public lighting.[33] There was no denying that, within this context, a contract to light and maintain public lamps at the old rate of £3.1s.8d. per lamp per annum for twenty years seemed reasonable in return for the restriction of the Alliance Gas Company or any other new competitor.[34]

Dublin oil gas station, 1824. The premises later became the Antient Concert Rooms, and is now the Academy Cinema, Pearse Street.

Councillor Fitzpatrick concluded by stating that the citizens 'should join and take the matter into their own hands, and they would be a large company, for they would have every shopkeeper in Dublin as shareholders'.[35]

This call for public enterprise was repeated by *The Freeman's Journal* in a series of articles designed to inflame public indignation and loosen private purses. On 8 August the main points of grievance were that

> the lighting of the city has been taken out of the hands of the municipal authorities and transferred to a private company, who are indirectly powered to tax the citizens at their pleasure. . . . The burdensome taxation in this instance falls principally upon the middle classes.

The power of the United General Gas Company was resented as was the weakness of the Alliance Gas Company.

On 10 August, it was stressed that Dublin had a corporation and that 'other cities, nay, even towns, and in Ireland too, have found public companies for the supply of gas to the inhabitants'. On 13 and 15 August consideration was given to the separate estimates of Sir John McNeill and a Mr Colquhoun for the erection and viability of a new and competing gasworks. On 16 August, it was observed that some citizens paid more for private gas consumption than was expended on entire streets nearby. On 21 August it was declared that 'every town of importance in England has the control of public lighting vested in the municipality . . . Every provincial town in Ireland whose inhabitants possess sufficient public spirit, by an elective body, controls the public lights'. Reference was made to the fact that Galway, Belfast, Athlone, Ballinastra, Clonmel and a dozen other towns throughout the kingdom did so, and to the fact that gas prices in Manchester were only half those of Dublin despite the variance in the price of coal which favoured Dublin. Indeed, conditions favourable to the consumer in Sheffield, Liverpool, Belfast, Wexford and Derry were reported as was the belief that the Limerick Consumers' Company had 'almost beaten the United General Gas Company out of the field' there.[36]

THE DUBLIN CONSUMERS' GAS COMPANY

The message was clear. The defence of present conditions was impossible, and the reaction was swift if not entirely predictable. On 21 September 1844 *The General Advertiser* published the prospectus of the Dublin Consumers' Gas Company offering 15,000 shares at £10 each upon deposit of £1 per share. However, unlike Limerick, the company was independent of the corporation, though its twenty-two member provisional committee consisted of such notable personages as the Lord Mayor, Councillor Thomas Kirwan and Daniel O'Connell.[37] To ensure local

adequate for the needs of Cork which used about a third of Dublin's quantity for public lighting and about a sixth for private lighting. However, Beamish was not a revolutionary. After making an unflattering comparison between conditions in Cork and Manchester, he admitted that 'no contest can take place in this city between rival establishments', and suggested a renewal of the contract with the (British-based) United General Gas Company for a further thirteen years at a reduced rate. Beamish was content to proclaim that prices were different in Cork and Manchester because social and economic conditions varied. Accordingly, he did not linger on the existence of two gas companies in Bristol, closer in size to Cork, and the relatively favourable conditions through competition there. Neither did he further stop to analyse the shortcomings of the United General Gas Company in relation to Cork.

However, the matter was by no means dropped. On 28 February 1844, *The Cork Examiner* published a collection of facts and figures with the idea that reduced prices meant more customers and larger profits.

> The effect which lowering the price of an article like gas has upon its consumption has never been more exemplified than in the statistics for Manchester; when in 1833 the charge was 10s. 6d. per thousand feet, the profits there were £8,292; in 1834 it was 10s. 3d. the profits £16,196; in 1837 8s. 6d. profits £18,712; in 1838 it was again lowered to 8s. 0d. and the profits realized £19,376 and in 1939 the price was 7s. 6d. the profits £24,658; the last reduction in 1840 was to 7s. 0d. and the profits increased to £24,738; in 1841 to £29,694 and in 1842 to £34,232.

On 15 April attention was given to Daniel O'Connell's opposition to the efforts of Sir Robert Peel in introducing two bills related to 'the most obnoxious tax' – the taxing of paving and lighting in Dublin. Considering the fact that the Wide Street Commissioners in Cork could only afford to pay £1,000 of the £2,862 owed to the United General Gas Company in 1847, it was but a matter of time before a similar stand would be taken there. The situation merely simmered in Cork for some years however, because the local population were powerless to do anything but complain. Thus, in 1845 criticism was directed at the Wide Street Board because it infringed upon the authority of the popular town council, consisted of members independent of rate-payers, collected as much as £12,000 a year in taxes, and entered into a thirteen-year contract with an English gas company (The United General).[40] Indeed, one writer to *The Cork Examiner* went so far as to infer that the relevant parties had their hands deep into the pockets of their fellow citizens.[41] But the United General continued to supply Cork with gas as it had done since 1826 while the responsible commissioners merely concerned themselves with matters of quantity and quality. Only in 1856, with the end of the contract in sight, was action taken.

THE CORK GAS CONSUMERS' COMPANY

On 22 May 1856 a public meeting was held in the City Court House for the purpose of considering the most practicable means of obtaining good gas at a reasonable price for the private consumer who paid as much as 6s. 8d. per 1,000 cubic feet of gas. Because the day had been sunny after a spell of bad weather, and possibly also because a number of sugar auctions had been held elsewhere at the same time, few but 'the largest and most respectable gas consumers of Cork' attended to object to 'the remarkable discrepancy' of 2s. 8d. between private and public lighting charges and 'the glaring and considerable injustice' of such a situation. However, the meeting was well reported in both *The Cork Constitution* and *The Cork Examiner* and was to lead ultimately to the formation of the Cork Gas Consumers' Company through the leadership of John Francis Maguire.

At the meeting, Maguire argued that the citizens of Cork were compelled to pay an exorbitant price for gas and referred to conditions in Whitehaven, Sunderland, Burnley, Sheffield, Belfast, Limerick, Liverpool, Birmingham, Galway, Ballymena, Kilkenny, Dublin and Bandon. His reference to Bandon was particularly convincing.

> In Bandon, one of the poorest towns in Ireland, a Gas Company was established by the Town Commissioners who got up works and paid for them, and at the present moment the cost of gas there is the same as in Cork . . . and Mr Sullivan stated that as soon as the debt incurred for building the gas premises was paid, which was now being done by instalments, the public would have the advantage in reduced rates.[42]

Apparently, Cork consumers were paying for the losses incurred by the United General Gas Company through competition in Dublin and Limerick.

Faced with a virtual barrage of information, Mr Gibbings, agent for the United General Gas Company and member of the corporation, simply blamed the corporation for not accepting the company's generous offer of 5s. 10d., a rate equal to that of Dublin. However, this was expertly brushed aside by Maguire's practiced rhetoric and humorous onslaught upon the inadequacies of the Old Widestreet Board. Maguire recalled that the commissioners had insisted on inspecting the quality of the gas supplied but had also agreed to give notice in writing to the gas company as to the time and place of inspection! Forgetting the efforts of Messrs Beamish, Hodder,

John Francis Maguire 1815-1872. Maguire was born in Cork, and became a noted journalist, politician and lawyer. He was called to the Bar in 1843. He became a Member of Parliament for Dungarvan in 1852, and in 1865 M.P. for Cork, a seat he held until his death. He founded *The Cork Examiner* newspaper. He was Lord Mayor of Cork for four terms. On the land question, important in his time, he took a nationalist viewpoint.

Lyons and Hagarthy in negotiating the contract with the United General Company in 1845, Maguire suggested that the relevant respectable gentlemen must have been half asleep or charmed by some person as he believed that any similar number of schoolboys in Cork could not have been party to such an agreement. As well as being dissatisfied with the cost of private lighting, he was clearly unhappy about the quality of gas produced in Cork:

> I assert that the illuminating power is not what it ought to be. I have been in printing offices of Cork and have seen compositors working by a light three inches broad and three inches high, and have known that they have been scarcely able to compose by its light.

Apparently, in Dundee the best cannel coal was used to supply all sectors of the community at 5s. 0d. or 5s. 6d. per 1,000 cubic feet of gas. Maguire believed that the cost and quality of gas in Cork were unfavourable because there was no competition and he advocated the purchase of the United General company by the corporation as sanctioned by law. Indeed, he went so far as to suggest that the United General Gas Company had recently installed iron retorts instead of the more modern, effective and cheaper clay variety promoted by M. Charpentier in Paris, in order to raise the valuation of the Cork works and thereby discourage any such bid by the corporation!

Maguire was not alone in his opposition to the London company at the meeting. A Mr Arnott asked why the mechanic and humble labourer hadn't 'his little jet' and hoped that the day might come 'when the rush-light and the farthing candle would be extinguished, and when the humble dwelling of the poor would have its gas' as 'there was no light so good as gas'.[43] A Mr Reidy had gone to the trouble of courting prosecution by stealing the burners of lamps in Laniley's Lane and Patrick Street in order to be able to discern the real rate of gas consumption per hour. Little wonder, then, that a writer to *The Cork Constitution* expressed the view that 'The meeting . . . shows that the Rate Payers are becoming alive to their conditions, they will no longer submit to the monopolising policy of any public company'.[44]

Of course, not everyone agreed with Maguire's grievances. For instance, a Dr Lyons, who was later to distinguish himself in the Crimean War, argued that it was only fair that gas for the public lights, irrespective of maintenance costs, should be cheaper than for private ones as financial savings, through careful conservation of gas, could be achieved by the individual consumer only.[45] Mr Gibbings, the United General's agent, eventually overcame his reluctance to enter public debate and undermined some of Maguire's assumptions regarding the relative conditions of gas production, consumption and sales in Cork in September 1856, with reference to gas conditions in Downpatrick, Clonmel, Dundalk, Newry, Portadown, Lurgan, Newtownards, Sligo, Derry, Dublin, Dungannon, Lisburn, Kilkenny, Armagh, Belfast, Ballymena, Galway and Nenagh.[46]

However, the days of the United General were numbered. Though the editorial policy of *The Cork Constitution* was opposed to the long-term effects of competing gas companies, its output on the question was minute when compared with that of its main rival, *The Cork Examiner.*[47] By 27 August 1856 Maguire had decided on the foundation of a second gas company and, as proprietor of *The Cork Examiner*, he proved to be a powerful adversary of the London-based concern and a popular advocate of local enterprise.

In relation to the establishment of the Cork Gas Consumers' Company, *The Cork Examiner* assumed a role similar to that of *The Freeman's Journal* in Dublin in 1844, underlining the significance of the press in such popular issues. Between the end of August and November 1856, a vigorous campaign was conducted to convince Cork consumers and citizens of the merits and viability of a new and local gas company. It began as a response to 'new excesses of benevolence' by the old company in reducing the price of gas and 'spreading all kinds of silly statement', and developed into a convincing argument on the historical, financial, legal, social and moral aspects of the question. The message was simple despite the rhetoric. Cork consumers would be foolish to continue paying for the expenses incurred by foreigners in fighting monopoly competitions in Dublin, Limerick and Plymouth when they could benefit from local production as experienced in Galway, Armagh and Dublin, and allowed by the Limited Liability Legislation of 1856.[48] Cork citizens and corporation were left in no doubt as to what course of action they should pursue with the *Examiner* declaring, on 26 November, that the Lord Mayor should be elected with a view to the all-important gas question. Thus, by December 1856, it was not a question of justification but of location, with sites in the City Park and in the neighbourhood of Blackpool being rejected in favour of a three-acre plot alongside the old gasworks at Albert Road.[49]

On 21 March 1857, at the ordinary half-yearly meeting of the United General Gas Company in London, the Secretary, D.W. Ogg, reported that Cork Corporation had accepted the tender of the local company to supply the public lights from January 1858. Ignorant of J.F. Maguire's prior successes in local matters of vagrancy, public sanitation and uniform weights for the sale of bread,[50] the shareholders were naturally surprised to hear that their tender had been rejected even though their prices had been 5s. 0d. per public lamp and 1s. 6d. per 1,000 cubic feet of gas for private consumption, cheaper than those of the new company. The Chairman, Mr J. O'Hanson, was particularly indignant about Cork's obvious ingratitude. After a brief reference to the longstanding and satisfactory relationship of the company with Cork, and a cursory explanation for the various prices charged there, he declared that

> in all large corporations there are restless spirits, and some of these seem to have fancied that our prices were exceedingly high, and that we were monopolists and extortioners. They have also complained of the quality of the gas but it is rather strange that all this should only have been found out at so recent a period. . . . I believe our works in Cork were never in better or more efficient state than they are at present moment – although they assert that our works are worn out and that our mains are defective . . . that the leakage is very excessive, being 30 percent. This is about as true as many of their other assertions. It is nothing approaching to that although our mains are travelling over a space of between forty and fifty miles.[51]

At the South Mall, on 10 June 1857, the Cork Gas Consumers' Company commenced laying the new pipes and mains which were to replace the thirty-six miles of service pipes and forty-three miles of mains laid by the United General Gas Company more than thirty years before. By then, *The Cork Examiner* had entered the second stage of its campaign to dislodge the English gas company. Information was given on the progress of the new works by the secretary, Denny Lane, the consultant engineer, George Anderson, and finally the manager, Henry Still.[52] Indeed, there was even some discussion on the proposed salary of the secretary, and an assurance that 'there will be scarcely any, if any, unpleasant odour from the works'.[53]

Meanwhile, *The Cork Constitution* had shown its true colours with the publication of a satirical extract from *The Journal of Gas Lighting*, published in London.[54] Though amusing, this was hardly convincing in that the promoters of the new company did not want profits as much as they wanted good gas:

> The citizens of Cork have never been singed with gas shares and unlike their London brethren, know nothing about . . . a 'no dividends day'. Moreover they are rather 'flush of cash' at the present moment and require bleeding to prevent an apoplectic determination to the head. Talk not to them of the advantages they enjoy from the investment of English capital in their gas works and by which they are left at liberty to invest all their own capital in promoting the industrial and commercial undertakings of their own city; away with such paltry argument! Money is not money if it is not Irish money, gas is not gas if it is not Irish gas. Shall Cork be dependent upon anything in the world but Cork for its own works? Perdition to the idea! Cork is a world in itself, self-located and self-sustained. Yes, Cork will burn its own coals, make its own iron and bricks, breed its own contractors, and under the influence of a Cork board of Cork directors, supply itself with genuine Cork gas to the delight of every citizen of Cork.

The article threatened the ultimate demise of the new company:

although a fanatical ebullition may, for a time, lead the corporation of Cork to prefer dear gas to cheap gas, yet as regards the consumer at large there is little doubt that in the end the 'breeches pocket' will carry the day. The old company has only to remain firm and make up its mind to a year or two of tribulation which will afterwards simply be recompensed by the unconditional submission of the little that will then remain of Mr Maguire's project; though we grieve to think that upon the gas consumers of Cork must eventually fall the payment in full of this native gas experiment.

In any case, by the end of May 1859, the new company had purchased the old works for the reasonable sum of £25,700,[55] and *The Cork Examiner* had dismissed the editor of *The Journal of Gas Lighting* as a first rate writer of fiction.[56]

The overall effect of the competition between the two companies, from 1856 to 1859, had been considerable in terms of gas sales and J.F. Maguire was naturally pleased with the outcome:

I must admit I was much surprised when I learned the extent of their trade. The fact is, the reduction in the price of gas has added enormously to its consumption in this city, developing in a few months a consumption which it might take years to attain under ordinary circumstances. We found in consequence of their diminished price, the other company had succeeded in maintaining, or rather creating a large consumption, and although that consumption was of little value to them it is of greatest consequence to us – for though they could only lose money at the price at which they were supplying the article . . . we must make largely by supplying the same customers at our moderate but still remunerative prices.[57]

Originally, the United General Gas Company had 1,600 meters in various Cork premises. However, within fourteen months of the new company's existence, this number had almost doubled with the United General maintaining 1,300 meters at 2s. 6d. per 1,000 cubic feet of gas and the Cork Gas Consumers' Company supplying 1,800 meters at 4s. 6d. per 1,000 cubic feet.[58] Accordingly, the initial rate of private gas consumption doubled between 1856 and 1859 to reach almost sixty million cubic feet.[59] The local achievement was considerable as amply reflected in an extract from *The Kilkenny Journal* complaining of gas conditions there in 1847:[60]

The citizens of Kilkenny are loud and unanimous in their complaints as regards the public and private gas lights of this city . . . Proprietors of many of the largest mercantile establishments in the city have stated to us that they will sign and seek signatures to a resolution pledging the citizens not to consume any gas in their warehouses and private dwellings unless the quality of gas be improved. We shall certainly lend our advocacy to that proceeding for we see no other way in which citizens can right themselves in this particular. It is too bad that they should pay such a high price as they are now paying for such inferior gas as is supplied to them.

Only four public institutions in Cork – the County Jail, Commercial Buildings, Workhouse, and Barracks – had braved the wrath of *The Cork Examiner* to enter contracts with the United General for short-term profits.[61] Little wonder that the Cork company rewarded the services of J.F. Maguire with £1,000 in March 1860.[62]

Opinions vary as to what influenced Maguire to found a rival gas company to the United General in Cork. Certainly, he had been influenced by earlier and similar opposition to the United General in Dublin and Limerick,[63] and by his witnessing fine quality gas privately produced and consumed on Lord Fermoy's estate.[64] However, he had also had experience of successful consumer competitiveness in London[65] and Clonmel. In 1865, Alderman McSwiney, a director of the Gas Company in Clonmel, recalled that J.F. Maguire had visited a friend in Clonmel while a gas agitation was going on in opposition to the charge of 10s. 0d. per 1,000 cubic feet of gas made by an English company there.[66] Apparently, Mr Maguire had not thought it beneath the city of Cork to borrow a leaf from the book of Clonmel, the capital of Tipperary, whose citizens had managed to halve their gas bill and double their illuminating power!

CLONMEL 1842-1849

In Clonmel, the agitation against the British Provincial Gas Light Company – which also owned works in Ayr, Gloucester, Hollywell, Hull, Norwich, Stoke, Shelton, and Townbridge – had begun in earnest on 14 January 1842 when a meeting was held at the Savings Bank to dispose of shares and finance the new Gas Consumers' Company. Clearly, the citizens were unhappy with 'the unsatisfactory manner in which, for a long period, the town and the consumer has been furnished by the old or English Company with the increasingly important article of gas both in respect of quality, quantity and regularity of supply as well as the very high rate at which it was furnished, added to the nearly utter hopelessness of obtaining redress in cases of complaint'.[67] After the company had refused 'a very liberal offer' for the works, a gas committee, consisting essentially of notable local merchants, made arrangements with a 'qualified and highly recommended Engineer', a James Colquhoun from Sheffield, for the erection and completion of a new works alongside the old. With the expenditure of £5,015 this was completed — with disc-shaped protruding

Detail in the yard of Clonmel Gas.

The gasholder at Clonmel, viewed from the managers' former home.

seals cast integrally with the pipes every three feet along their length in order to distinguish the new company's mains from those of its older competitor and restrain the latter company from tapping their opponent's mains inadvertently or by design. The new consumer company was formed on 24 September 1842 and, after strong competition, the old works purchased.

LIMERICK 1841–1880

The speedy success of the Clonmel Gas Consumers' Company (under the direction of such personages as Charles Bianconi) may have given John Francis Maguire of Cork encouragement in his stand against the United General Gas Company. This is certainly more than may be said of the progress of the rival gas company to the United General in Limerick. Despite the generous predictions of *The Freeman's Journal* and *The Cork Examiner* during the mid-nineteenth century,[68] the corporation gas company did not succeed in defeating the British-based concern until 1879 when it purchased the works of the United General for £26,000.[69] The agitation in Limerick for a second gas company had begun as early as February 1841 with a petition to the Commissioners of the Parish of Saint Michael, supported by more than a hundred signatures and led by Alexander Brothers, complaining that

> we have been, for a considerable time, labouring under the two-fold disadvantage of paying a very high price for inferior Light, and the complaint having lately become general throughout the Parish, the undersigned having satisfactorily ascertained that GAS may be obtained, producing a clear and brilliant light, far superior to that which the Parish has been supplied, and perfectly inoffensive, at a reduction of from Ten to Fifteen per Cent on the present prices.[70]

The English company had supplied gas meters only in a few isolated cases and charged what they wanted per burner so that in no single instance was the price of gas less than 10s. 0d. per 1,000 cubic feet, although neighbouring cities were being supplied at 6s. 0d. and 7s. 0d. per 1,000 feet.[71] Accordingly, a meeting was held at the Parish Office, Upper Cecil Street, on 4 March 1841, to consider the possible formation of a competing consumer company. Shortly afterwards, the newly formed city corporation purchased premises for the manufacture of gas with the aid of a loan of £24,000. The new company charged 5s. 0d. per 1,000 cubic feet of gas and secured the contract for public lighting.[72]

Evidently, competition between the two gas companies in Limerick was sensible if spirited, with the United General Gas Company being represented by the popular Mark T. O'Shaughnessy, and even taking legal action against the City Corporation for the value of the old public lamp pillars in 1856.[73] In any case, both parties resigned themselves to the existence of two competing gas companies in Limerick until 1876 when the Corporation Gas Company had to restrict the number of its consumers and give serious consideration to the prospect of expansion. In 1876, after the British company refused to sell its works to the corporation, W. Waterfield, engineer of the Dublin Alliance Company, recommended the expenditure of more than £2,000 on a new set of condensers, governor, purifiers and gas holder.[74] However, by December 1877 the United General had changed its mind about the sale of its Limerick company and entered into negotiations with the corporation. The merits of purchase were outlined by R.P. Spice of London to the effect that the cost of production and distribution of gas would be cheaper under one administration, and that no money would leave Limerick in respect of profits, but only for raw materials necessary for production.[75] Thus, by 1880 Limerick had only one gas company, and on 17 May 1881 *The Journal of Gas Lighting* noted 'a marked progress in the united undertakings' and felt that 'the Corporation might be excused for feeling intense remorse that a state of competition should have been allowed to exist in the gas supply of their town throughout so many years'.

GAS AGITATION IN DUBLIN 1847–1878

A single company had also come to dominate in Dublin by 1867, despite the express desire of the citizens to promote competition as reflected in legislation of 1847 which recognised the bonding of the Dublin Consumers' Gas Company with the older Alliance Company, but refused to tolerate any further expansion through purchase by them of the United General Gaslight Company.[76] On 16 July 1866 this Act was repealed, the Alliance and Dublin Consumers' Gas Company amalgamated with the new Commercial Gas Company, and the Dublin works of the United General transferred to the resultant company which retained the title Alliance & Dublin Consumers' Company. (The Commercial Gas Company of Ireland Limited – registered under the 1862 Companies Act, to supply gas to Dublin, Kingstown and Bray, on 4 February 1864 – had been founded and supported on the principle of competitiveness among neighbouring gas companies, and based, to some degree, on the example of Cork.[77])

The movement towards amalgamation, which culminated in the unification of three Dublin gas companies, had been led by Sir John Gray who wielded a greater knowledge of the technicalities of gas lighting than his fellow newspaper proprietor John Francis Maguire. Gray was already well known as 'the life and soul of the great Vartry project for supplying . . . Dublin with pure and wholesome water'.[78] While others compared Dublin with cities throughout Scotland, England and Ireland, Gray went a step further than an unflattering comparison between conditions in Dublin and Edinburgh. He explained that the 13-candle gas supplied by the Dublin gas companies lost half its illuminating power through the use of batwing and fishtail burners. As the quality of gas depended on the type of coal consumed by the gas companies as much as on the type of burner employed by customers, he preferred to promote the use of expensive cannel coal than the alternative widespread use of awkward argand burners.

In referring to the gas agitation in Dublin in 1865, George Anderson, engineer to the new company, contended that 'no town was well supplied with gas unless it was gas of a kind that could be introduced into every ordinary room not only of the wealthy but of the humbler classes so that the artisan, after the labour of the day, could sit down to read by good light'. Anderson also declared that 'he never saw exhibited such grand intelligence in considering the question as was now displayed'.[79] Certainly, the existence of agitation was hardly novel or surprising given the formation of more than five separate gas companies in Dublin since the early twenties, the gentlemanly arrangement between the two established gas companies to divide and rule the city, and the expiration of the 1845 contract between the city corporation and the Hibernian (United General) Gas Company for public lighting in January 1865.[80] However, what was surprising to some extent was the fact that when he repeated Sir John Gray's innocent comparison between Dublin and Edinburgh, a man of Anderson's standing in the British Gas industry ignored the differences between the two cities. There was, at first glance, a major discrepancy between a charge of £0 19s.9d. per lamp per year in Edinburgh and one of £3 13s.6d. in Dublin. However, Edinburgh was lit at a rate of 2 cubic feet for 2,810 hours per year as compared with Dublin's 4,573 hours at double the rate per hour. Moreover, in Edinburgh the maintenance costs for the lamps was paid not by the gas company, as in Dublin, but by the corporation as in London. Likewise, Edinburgh did not incur the same transport expenses as Dublin with coal practically at its doorstep.[81] The gas question was obviously a matter of perspective.

Dublin – Consolidation and Amalgamation

On 30 March 1865, T.M. Gresham, chairman of the Alliance & Dublin Consumers' Company, declared that 'For years, he and other shareholders had not got a dividend . . . but as soon as they got a fair dividend . . . a clamour was raised, and they were told that they were making too much money, that they ought to do this and ought to do that, and if they did not, that an opposition company would be started which would take from them many of their customers . . . it was a melancholy thing that this kind of opposition should be adopted, it was [also] so with respect to railways'.[82] Yet, the gas movement in favour of the Commercial Gas Company was not so much against the native Alliance & Consumers' Company as against the foreign United General as suggested by Sir John Gray's remark that 'It would be a great calamity if there should be three competing companies . . . a large number of retired merchants' widows and the trustees of orphans had invested in a very profitable and successful native company – the Alliance Gas Company – and everything should be done to sustain it as being a native company, and to protect it from unjust, and what might be called illegitimate, competition'.[83] As it happens, the works of the United General in Dublin (i.e. the Hibernian, Kingstown and Bray Gas Companies) were sufficient to supply all the districts in which they were situated and were very well placed. Indeed, in 1864 a British civil engineer named J.G. Barlow considered the gas produced by the company as of considerable purity and superior to the average of that supplied in London from Newcastle coal.[84]

The major grievances which impeded the progress of this British company in Dublin were related to cost rather than quality. It was widely felt that the company had burdened the private consumer unnecessarily through ambitious and extravagant conduct — in purchasng the old Dublin gas companies for £216,000,[85] and in agreeing to incur a loss for public lighting in order to secure a practical monopoly. In 1845 the United General had entered a twenty-year contract to supply gas to the corporation at 2s. 4½d. per 1,000 cubic feet of gas, on the understanding that the corporation would not grant the power of supplying Dublin with gas to any other body.[86] At the time, the charge for private consumption was 7s. 6d. per 1,000 cubic feet. Thus, in 1865, it was assumed that gas to the private consumer would have been cheaper in Dublin if the United General had not entered into an underhand agreement with the city corporation. Indeed, it was also believed that the United General was supporting its competitive position in Limerick 'by dipping their hands into Dublin'.[87] With such a reputation, the United General had little future in Dublin. In any case, the United General failed to secure the parliamentary support necessary for the modernisation of its works in 1865, while the Commercial Gas Company survived a number of parliamentary skirmishes and the Alliance & Dublin Consumers' Gas Company gained the contract for public lighting.

Native Monopoly – Public Versus Private Ownership

In the wake of the United General's demise, it was hardly surprising that the two victorious local companies should combine to share a single and more adequate distribution network. In 1866 popular opinion was generally in favour of the amalgamation, *The Dublin Builder*, for instance, viewing it as 'a step in the right direction, and one which we doubt not will prove equally beneficial to the consumer and the new company'.[88] The company had entered a ten-year contract with the corporation to supply 16-candle gas at £3 3s. 0d. per lamp per annum, and the committee of the municipal council had predicted a saving of £1,000 per year through reform of old street lamps, metering methods, lighting techniques and the employment of the city corporation in lighting, cleansing, and extinguishing the public lamps. All boded well with the secretary of the company, John Stevenson, apologising for any initial inconvenience brought about through the erection of a telescopic gas holder, 106 feet in diameter, at Sir John Rogerson's Quay, the laying of a grand trunk main, 36 inches in diameter, from the works to Carlisle Bridge, and the use of a new set of dry purifiers of larger dimension.[89]

However, by November 1871 *The Irish Builder* had changed its perspective on the question.[90]

> It at last becomes necessary to know whether the Gas Consumers' Company of the city are really an irresponsible body as well as one enjoying a complete monopoly. When we had two distinct companies in Dublin one acted as a check against the other's intolerance; but it seems now that we must submit, not only to be cheated, but to be snubbed if we remonstrate against a system that amounts to very little short of a public patent extortion. . . . . If there were rival companies in Dublin we would have better light and a little more courtesy and good breeding shown on the part of the officials of the gas company.

Apparently, the Gas Company was providing 'poor' quality gas and cutting off the supply of struggling shopkeepers who were unable to pay their bills on time and had no longer any alternative means of public supply.

Certainly, the new company was running into difficulties, as suggested by the fact that it applied for an act of parliament in order to reduce the illuminating standard of gas, in February 1871, only to concede a 25 percent higher illuminating power in August 1871.[91] During 1872 *The Irish Builder* continued its crusade against poor lighting and even wondered, in April, why it was 'that all this is forgotten or ignored by the very journalists that complained [in 1864] and who are now bound in consideration for business reasons that need no particular mention'.[92] (This must certainly have been a reference to Sir John Gray, proprietor of *The Freeman's Journal*, who had been a director of the Commercial Company and continued as such with the new Alliance Company.) However, the wrath of *The Irish Builder* was not entirely spent on the company or muted journalists. On November 1872, in giving consideration to William Cotton's suggestion that the corporation should take over the management of the Dublin gas supply, it condemned the corporation as well as the company:

> We' have no objection in the least to see the gas system managed by corporate authority, provided that a reform is first effected in the municipal representation of Dublin. Until a corporate reform takes place and fresh blood is infused into the weak and mischievous councils of our present Corporation it would be unsafe to entrust them with performing new duties. . . . The Corporation should first get out of debt, and try to perform the undertaking it had already pledged itself to perform before increasing its burdens and further taxing the city. . . . The gas supply of Dublin is dear and nasty, and under corporate management it would, we fear, little improve, unless a corporate reform is effected at the same time.[93]

On 15 December it declared that

> If the Corporation of this city were like any other Corporation in England, who have taken the gas supply into their hands, free of debt, we would have no serious objections to raise. Here, however, the citizens stand face to face with a Corporation who are a disgrace to Great Britain, and who have dragged down and degraded our city by the meanest and most shameful artifices, to cover their incapacity and neglect. With a taxation of 10s. 0d. in the pound, the city is in filth and decay, and a prey at any moment to a raging epidemic. . . . In the midst of all this job after job is hatched, to hide over a financial difficulty on the one hand, and earn the wages of betrayal on the other.[94]

Clearly, the journalists in question believed that many members of the corporation were either shareholders or directors of the gas company and that the proposed corporation acquisition of the means of gas production was 'a gigantic corporate swindle' to be paid for by the ordinary ratepayers.

At the time, the argument of the Corporation's Superintendent of Public Lighting – that the poorer classes were deprived of the advantages of gas lighting through the ineptitude of management and past expenditure in entering parliamentary contests and in purchasing and reforming former Dublin gasworks – was given serious consideration. There was no denying that the ratio of consumer to non-consumer in Dublin was 1:20 as compared to 1:6 in Manchester where the corporation had reduced the price of gas from 5s. 0d. per 1,000 cubic feet to 3s. 0d. within twenty years.[95] In Dublin, as W.F. Cotton observed, the only change in price had been from 16-candle gas at 5s. 0d. in 1852 to 20-candle gas at 5s. 6d. per 1,000 cubic feet in 1872, despite a doubling in the rate of gas consumption. With a transfer of the works to the corporation and the expenditure of £13,000 in putting the works and mains in proper order the situation might change for the better, or so the corporation argued, and the relevant authorities in the company were happy to concede. However, the attempt to carry through parliament the necessary legislation failed,[96] so that *The Irish Builder* could declare, in May 1873, that 'the projectors were stranded and wrecked'.[97] Apparently, the only positive outcome of the affair was that W.F. Cotton was appointed secretary and allowed the specified £13,000 in order to put his recommendations related to production into practice.

Shareholders Versus Consumers

As suggested by John McEvoy's pamphlet, *The Dublin Gas Question,* published in 1876, W.F. Cotton found it easier to analyse the inadequacies of the gas situation than to alleviate them. From June 1873 to October 1876, £32,000 was expended by the company on its capital account. Of this, £20,830 was given to new buildings, manufacturing plant, machines and condensers connected with the manufacture of gas, or spent on new mains and service pipes connected with its distribution. However, the lighting situation did not improve through the substitution of 16-candle for 20-candle gas – as instituted by legislation of 1874 and brought about by a 30 percent increase in the price of ordinary coal in 1873 – because more gas had to be consumed to provide the accustomed standard of lighting. Moreover, while the cost of such 16-candle gas per 1,000 cubic feet was 3s. 11d. in Belfast and 4s. 9d. in Cork, it was 5s. 0d. in Dublin, the same as Limerick, with Limerick's smaller consumption and greater distance from coal fields to explain its humble position.[98] Indeed, the situation was so embarrassing that when Messrs Neville, Norwood and Gray were sent, by Dublin Corporation, to give evidence before a parliamentary session on local government in Ireland, and to be cross-examined by Sir Arthur Guinness and Mr. Brooks, in 1875, they failed to define or remember the actual price of gas in Dublin.[99] Neville, the borough engineer, did not know anything about gas while Norwood, counsel for the corporation, simply forgot the relevant details and Sir John Gray concentrated on the relative cheapness of public lighting and lamplighters in Dublin without reference to standards of illumination elsewhere or the cost of private gas consumption in Dublin.

In any case, in October 1876 John McEvoy had little difficulty in making convincing comparisons which showed Dublin in a poor light. He began with the question of coal transportation as found in London and Dublin, and based his argument on evidence given by Mr. Livesey, Manager of the South Metropolitan Company, in the course of an enquiry before the London Division Commissioners in 1874. At the time, this company supplied gas at 3s. 0d. per 1,000 feet after burning 5 percent Wigan or Welsh cannel and 95 percent common Newcastle coal. The argument was reasonably simple. Freights of cannel favoured Dublin while freights of Newcastle favoured

London by as much as four shillings. However, the London coal was subject to city dues of a shilling and a penny per ton compared with the 13s. 4d. shippage and anchorage dues paid in Dublin for a whole cargo of several hundred tons. Accordingly, the actual difference between them was three shillings per ton. However, this only represented four pence per 1,000 feet extra on Dublin gas and by no means excused a charge of five shillings. Indeed, it was difficult to justify such a charge when

> The business of the two companies is nearly equal: the South Metropolitan selling 820,000,000, the Dublin Alliance 750,000,000 feet per annum. Their districts, too, closely resemble one another – the South Metropolitan being largely suburban extending to Croydon and other suburban towns and having . . . several miles of mains for which a very small revenue is derived. They have not many large mills, factories or other large consumers. The cheapness of the gas has led to its introduction into nearly all the houses in the district and instead of serving the 1:20, as in Dublin, it serves the 1:10 of the population.[100]

John McEvoy combined the views of Sir John Gray in 1865 and William Cotton in 1872 by suggesting that more cannel coal should be used as in Belfast, and advocating a reduction in price in order to boost sales.

However, McEvoy went much further in highlighting the fact that the Dublin firm Messrs Manders and Powell could produce gas at 2s. 3d. per 1,000 feet 'with all the disadvantages of working on a small scale and of carting coal and other materials across the city'. There was obviously something wrong with the purchasing department of the Alliance company as it paid as much as £1 7s. 10d. per ton of Newcastle coal when it could be had at Dublin Quay for eighteen shillings a ton and delivered by profit-making concerns to any part of the city for £1 3s.6d. per ton. Moreover, the shortcomings in this area were compounded somewhat by the shortfall in the average yield from residuals as suggested by Dublin's poor return of 33 percent as compared with London's 53 percent.[101] However, the central question was whether the shareholders or the consumers should pay for the company's obvious inadequacies. Apparently, the Alliance had every intention of declaring a 10 percent dividend in the very near future, and McEvoy naturally inquired as to whether the consumer should be surcharged 25 percent to 30 percent on his gas to constitute a 10 percent dividend for the company, or the company content itself with a smaller dividend and sell gas at its 'real' value instead. He advised the latter, thus promoting cheap gas, and he further traced the financial and legislative conditions which had lent themselves to the advantage of the shareholders since the coal famine of 1873, and quoted from *The Journal of Gas Lighting* to the effect that the resultant and inevitable founding of a rival gas company would involve a shameful waste of money.[102]

In 1876, agitation on the gas situation was considerable with even the tamed *Freeman's Journal* insisting that prices were too high despite the best efforts of company directors and staff.[103] Indeed, McEvoy's pamphlet in October 1876 resulted in part from a series of conflicting letters on the question, published in *The Freeman's Journal* during February and March of that year, and favourably inclined towards a defence of the company in the face of repeated but weak attacks by one letter-writer who signed as 'Observer'. At the end of February 1876, 'Observer' noted that the basic criticism of the gas company by W.F. Cotton in 1872 still held true and was 'sufficient for a Citizen's Company to go to Parliament on'.[104] Basing his figures on the 1872 report and some other questionable assumptions,[105] he even calculated an annual loss of £43,750 to the citizens of Dublin and translated its value into more concrete terms:

> It would be enough to cleanse the Liffey – to rebuild Carlisle Bridge ten times over – to pave the city with wood or asphalt – light twelve public lamps for every one that now makes darkness visible – to pay for more than half the poor in our workhouse – to establish a line of transatlantic steamers – erect habitable houses for our artisan population, instead of the fever nests in which they at present reside – to endow a National University – to reduce the rates 1s. 9d. in the pound . . . This is what the citizens are throwing away.[106]

However, while not denying what could be done with £43,750, fellow letter-writers 'A' and 'Fair Play' rejected 'Observer's' thesis. According to 'A', Dublin was not the only city in the British Isles to suffer an increase in gas charges and endure a reduction in illuminating power.[107] Indeed, legislation dictating the type of burner to be used in evaluating the required standard of gas made the company a victim of the coal situation rather than a master of the gas question, or so 'Fair Play' argued.[108]

On 3 March, *The Freeman's Journal* published a lengthy letter from 'Fair Play' which was remarkable for the reasonableness with which it condemned 'Observer's' failure to use current facts and figures, while defending the gas company and its secretary, W.F. Cotton:

> In passing, I may say that although everything stated by Mr Cotton was undoubtedly true, nevertheless it must be remembered that at the time Mr Cotton wrote as an adverse critic, and no one knows better than 'Observer' that a critic, though he speaks the truth, yet he will go to the limits of it, and put everything as much as possible in the light that will best represent his . . . view and the object for which he writes. Mr Cotton, at that time, looked at the subject at a distance and without the intimate knowledge of details that he since

acquired. He made statements of facts then present – he formed his opinion to the best of his ability. . . . Much that he presumed has come to pass; much more will follow; and if every promise made by him was not realised it was because he could not foresee difficulties that the future might bring forth, and because facts are more stubborn than figures . . . the report of Mr Cotton, now being several years old, cannot be an authority for . . . comparisons between present existing companies or . . . adverse arguments thereon.[109]

'Fair Play' took the novel approach of reminding all concerned that the citizens were as responsible as the shareholders in causing the capital of the company to be excessive through promotion of rival companies and related parliamentary and technological expense in the past. Thus, all criticism was banished in the hope that 'the present Dublin gas company may proceed in the career of success opened to it by the energy and honesty of its present directors and . . . become one of the few Irish successful enterprises, and another proof of the advantage of Home Rule'.

James Kirby – the Consumers' Advocate

However, not everyone could share 'Fair Play's' optimism or his reluctance to compare Dublin with cities more fortunate in regard to gas supply. John McEvoy was obviously one, James Kirby but another. For some unknown reason *The Freeman's Journal* refused to print any of Kirby's somewhat repetitive but highly critical and informative letters on the gas situation in Dublin,[110] and so the task of publication fell to *The Irish Builder* and *The Irish Times*.

According to himself, Kirby was instrumental in mobilising effective opposition to the proposed corporation acquisition of the gas company in 1873.[111] In any event, for more than a decade afterwards, he sought, found, and presented evidence of company and corporation corruption and incompetence. The core of his argument was that the corporation contained too many members with vested interests in the profitable sale of gas, who accordingly failed to protect the ratepayers from the obvious burdens of a monopolised and essential product. From this, the tentacles of his argument slowly spread to embrace all aspects of the question and educate the general public on such basic gas issues as those pertaining to meters, pressure, and inspection. His observations were not without foundation and were worthy of serious consideration if only because he promised a considerable saving on rates and escaped company and corporation condemnation whilst doing so.

Taken thematically, the riveting precision of Kirby's piecemeal argument is evident. On 20 April 1874 he complained of gas measures being incorrect to the extent of one-seventh of the whole gas rental and to the tune of about £30,000 a year, while noting that common air was mixed with the gas and forced through the meters.[112] On 27 August 1876 he highlighted Justice Morris's distrust of gas meters in the case of the Alliance Company versus Robert Taaffe, while promoting the dry-meter because 'there could be less trickery' (the water level of the wet-meter had to be kept at the right elevation if the customer or the company were not to be robbed).[113] He then pointed out that more than half the gas meters sealed in the city department were used in the surrounding townships, and asked 'Why then are the city rates burdened with keeping up this Hanover-Street establishment and staff for doing work, more than half the benefit of which is derived by parties not residing in the city or contributing to the city rates?'

On 29 May 1878 he stressed that the pressure on the gas supply should be similar to that under which the meters were tested.[114] On 29 October 1878 he declared that the gas in the mains was three times as much as that required and resulted in much wastage and expense.[115] On 25 June 1879 he demolished any idea that much pressure was justified by reason of terrain and the necessity of supplying the townships, while noting that 'on every occasion when the price of gas was reduced during the past four years, the pressure on it has been increased'.[116] On 12 May 1881 he further argued that the current minimum pressure of 2½ inches was four times too much for the city and concluded with a comparison between the situation in Dublin and Bristol:

> The gas district in Bristol is one-third greater in superficial area than that of the city of Dublin, and it is much more hilly. The most distant point of consumption in this city from the gasworks is but two and a half miles, while in Bristol it is four miles. Still 16-candle gas can be profitably distributed there under a pressure of 1 inch at three shillings per 1,000 ft.[117]

On 28 July 1882 he revealed the significance of such excess pressure through reference to a report of the British Association in 1878.[118] Here, it was shown that

> at half-inch pressure, a union jet consuming five cubic feet of gas per hour, gave a light equal to 28.47 candles, while at 1½ inch pressure the light was only equal to 21.14 candles, a proportion of 100 to 74. That, in cases of smaller consumption of gas per hour, the numbers obtained are still more startling – that this is exceeded when still higher pressure is used, and that the loss of light is greater with common than with cannel gas.

Thus, Kirby advocated the introduction of regulators to reduce and maintain the pressure at 1 2/10 inches because 'not only are the consumers of gas deprived by excessive pressure of the amount of light they are charged for, but, from the same cause their meter indicates the transit of greater or lesser bulks of gas according as the pressure on the gas supply is increased or diminished.'

As if the cumulative effects of these technical observations were not enough, Kirby openly condemned company practice and corporation supervision. For instance, he reminded the ratepayers that their representatives decided to purchase the gasworks in 1873, despite the advice of eminent British engineers who considered

> Dublin gasworks as being the worst constructed in the world – that a very large outlay of money would be required to put them in proper working order; and even after such an expenditure, that it was doubtful if the concern could be made to pay, the gas district being so scattered.[119]

He also found fault with the fact that thirty-three of the thirty-five members of the corporation managed to vote in favour of the appointment of Cotton's brother-in-law, Mr O'Connor, as city gas inspector at £300 per annum.[120] He naturally believed that 'for some time past, any question affecting the gas company's interest was neutral ground on which the majority of the members of the Corporation, liberal and conservative, economist and home-ruler, all united and worked harmoniously together . . . to keep the gas consumers in ignorance of the means by which the amounts of the gas bills were increased'.[121]

Kirby pointed to the fact that the city inspector, only eight months after his appointment, 'assisted the gas company in defrauding the public rates of about £1,000 by permitting 4 ft. burners to be placed in all the public METERED lamps five months before the company could remove ALL the burners consuming much less gas per hour in the other lamps, and replace them with 4 ft. burners'.[122] He objected to the payment of £123 17s. 9d. for reverification of the Dublin copies of standard gas measures without payment of compensation by the gas company for many years of incorrect metering.[123] He further condemned the payment of lamplighter's wages to two individuals who had never lit a public lamp in their lives, and even unearthed a case of jobbery in regard to the practice of gas fitting.[124] Indeed, he concluded that 'if Judas Iscariot was a member of Dublin Corporation, he would not have thrown away the thirty pieces of silver', and asserted that the public character of the gas company for honest dealing 'closely resembled the coffin of Mahomet hanging somewhere, difficult to find, between heaven and earth'.[125]

Kirby did not confine himself to religious analogies or content himself with astute, and sometimes exaggerated, observations. He suggested that the gas company should supply, clean, light and extinguish all the public lamps without any added charge, the Board of Trade or the Board of Works should assume the remaining supervisory duties of the inept Department of Public Lighting at the company's expense, and the corporation should apply itself to the provision of public libraries.[126] It was a tall order from someone without power. Without corporation support or widespread discontent, however, he must have realised that this was not a viable policy nor, indeed, an attractive alternative to either the founding of a rival gas company or the acquisition of the gasworks by the corporation. Like McEvoy, Kirby faced a dilemma. He opposed corporation management of the gas supply on the grounds that the situation would not improve, while he rejected the possibility of founding a rival company through knowledge of Dublin's past experience of competing companies and expensive amalgamations. There was little left for him to do other than complain and look forward to the growth of electoral consciousness,[127] or the improvement and introduction of electric lighting.[128] Most ratepayers only became conscious of the gas question when the contract for public lighting came up for renewal, in such years as 1866 and 1876, while any dissatisfied large manufacturer had the option of installing his own generating plant. Little wonder that the gas company refused to answer public charges and did little more than warn newspaper proprietors of the need to measure their words for fear of heavy damages in a court of law.[129]

THE ROLE OF NEWSPAPERS

It was no accident that newspaper men had a tendency to stir up trouble for gas companies as suggested by the publication, in *The Newry Telegraph, of* the following:

> We feel it to be a duty to call attention to the quality of the gas now supplied to the consumers of the town. It is at times sadly wanting in illuminating power and as the night advances becomes 'a dim religious light'. We are special sufferers for we are called upon to do important work when the immense majority of the townspeople, after the day's toil, enjoy a refreshing sleep. After midnight the gas is very bad and sometimes we feel tempted to anathematise the gas manager and all his works.[130]

In any case, gas was an ideal subject for controversy as there was always reason for complaint in that the mode of production and supply could always be improved, the quality produced always bettered, the price charged always reduced, the hours covered for public lighting always extended, and the area supplied always widened. To begin with, problems of supply were encountered, as suggested by the loud denunciation of 'the gas man' in April 1836 by *The Wexford Freeman*:

Clonmel Gasworks – a gas light long past its prime.

The contractor for supplying the quays with gas has lately been in the habit of taking a liberty in our streets – which puts to the blush all former infringements on civic rights. He declares whenever he pleases, any street he pitches upon in a state of blockade, places a rope or chain across it, digs a deep trench through it whole length and, without saying why or wherefore, renders it impossible for nearly a whole day. This is bad enough in all conscience; but were it the extent of the gas man's modesty and had he the honesty to leave the streets as he found them, we should be inclined to pass it over. Indeed, an expectation that he would make good the grievous damage he caused did induce us to pass it over the last time. How great was our astonishment to find that instead of replacing the well formed Macadamised pavement he disturbed he caused the trenches to be filled with rubbish thrown in the loosest manner, and the consequence was the streets were all in places complete sloughs. He has again commenced tearing up the streets, and we trust our worthy Mayor will oblige him to leave them at least as good as he found them.[131]

(The *Freeman* was particularly concerned about the state of the street in front of its own office).[132]

Then, there were also problems of inadequate supply to worry about. For instance, *The Galway Mercury* was requested, in October 1845, 'by several inhabitants who are desirious of preserving the lives of their fellow creatures, to call attention to the practice which now exists, with a view to its remedy, of not sending out the men to light the public lamps, at the New Dock, until all the other parts of the town are completed' as it resulted in almost two hours of total darkness there after nightfall.[133] Even so, Galway was obviously more advanced than Sligo, as suggested by the observation of *The Sligo Champion* in August 1881 that, due to a resolution of the Harbour Commissioners, lamps had been erected and supplied along the quay so that 'passengers will now no longer have to grope their way in utter darkness and to the imminent danger of their lives'.[134] Apparently, there were many mothers and widows available who would have appreciated the service much sooner.

There were obviously instances of incompetence and neglect. In January 1885 a contributor to *The Tyrone Courier* asked why factory employees and others in Dungannon had 'to grope their way through dark streets to their different places of work' between five and six in the morning when the ratepayers were charged on the assumption that half the gas lamps were kept burning until half-past-six.[135] In actual fact, the extinguishing of public lamps from half-past-four in the morning had begun the previous year without adverse criticism.[136] However, this was mild abuse when read in the context of other reports. On 29 May 1879 *The Tuam Herald* reported that 'every night for the past fortnight . . . not a lamp in the whole town was lighted, although the evenings were as dark as Cerberus'.[137] In November

1860 *The Wexford Constitution* drew attention to the pool of stagnant water 'besides the Gas Works and immediately behind the Militia Barracks, the insalubrious effluvium off which, impregnated as it is with a vast amount of noxious gases, must be very injurious to the health of those who live in its immediate neighbourhood'.[138] Apparently, the barrack warden had lodged a complaint against it damaging the health of his troops, which the corporation had seen fit to ignore!

There is little doubt that gasworks were not appreciated by those who lived in their immediate vicinity. One opponent to the new company in Kingstown in 1865 argued, for instance, that 'gasworks would be a nuisance to the neighbourhood at all times from whatever quarter the wind would blow', and declared that he would never believe that they would be anything but a nuisance to the districts in which they were placed. Neighbours were not unknown to complain. For instance, the minutes of the Carrickfergus Gas Company of 27 June 1898 record Edward McCallister's request to build a four-inch brick wall on top of the existing wall of the gasworks, and the directors' inability to grant him his request! Of course, there were worse dangers than smells, fumes and dust, as suggested by the fact that in February 1860 the timber yard of Mr Connolly, 38 Sir John Rogerson's Quay, Dublin, went on fire owing to the over-heating of bricks of the walls adjoining the Alliance Gas Works. This could prove exceptionally problematic when, as in the case of spontaneous combustion of coal at Newtownards Gasworks in 1875, there was no fire brigade to rely on — only the local population with buckets of water in hand! Even so, the response to the erection and existence of gasworks was by no means uniformly negative. In Newtownards itself, in 1870, for instance, the erection of the second gasworks was warmly welcomed because of its construction on a site usually frequented by local vagabonds! Indeed, the Company Minutes of the Dungannon Gas Company, for 8 September 1885, record an application by Mr Jack Orr 'for portion of the field of the Gas Works to convert it into a Tennis Yard', and the directors' decision to charge 1d. rent per week for the privilege! There were certainly differing approaches to environmental issues.

In popular estimation, matters related directly to finance were considered more serious. In October 1882, S.J. O'Brien noted the considerable discrepancies in public gas consumption in Kildare since 1876, and provided the following tabulation to prove that meters were at fault.

Year	c.ft.	Year	c.ft.
1876	2,916	1881	6,150
1878	3,881	1882	8,184[139]
1880	4,244		

The relevant authorities decided to impose fines on any such future infringement of company commitments. A similar policy had been adopted in Ennis the previous year.[140] Naturally, the question of imposing such fines was a fruitful ground for argument as reflected in a report by *The Drogheda Argus* of February 1885:

A dozen of lamps were reported as being found in darkness during the time stipulated for lighting. Explanations were read from the Company. They were all right when lighted. They were in the majority of instances put out by the storm. The gas was pumping out of the burners the whole time . . . Mr Farrell said that their duty there was to ensure that the public would get the benefit of the light that was paid for and, that being so, he would certainly move that all the fines be recorded against the Company as they do not think fit to have a man to go round and relight them. Was the town to be left in darkness and no more about it? That was a way of doing the people's business he would be no party to. Mr Mangan [said] . . . You wouldn't have a man to stand under the lampost all night? Mr Farrell [said] . . . The gas company consider it better to pay fines than to employ a man to relight the lamps and I would let them take that choice and submit to the fines.[141]

Comparative Analysis in the Newspapers

The area of comparative analysis was the one in which most gas companies suffered most. In May 1865, 'a gas consumer' in Carrickfergus moaned:

We look around us and see other towns . . . lighted up with gas as rich in illuminating power as that in our own town and considerably lower in price than it is with us. . . . When the prospectus was first issued we anticipated . . . that if the gas would not be cheaper it would at least be as cheap as in other towns of the same population. This we find, on inquiry, not to be the case, for in other towns of the same population the price of gas is often 20 percent below that of our own. That is not only contrary to the prospectus, issued in 1854, but also to the sentiments and decisions of the directors of the time who stated they would be satisfied with 5 percent or so whereas the percentage often averages fourteen or fifteen.[142]

More significantly, after this vague comparison and some words of wisdom regarding the central role of cheap prices in boosting sales, he asked: 'Surely the inhabitants are not so blind to their own interest as not to use a little exertion in getting their gas reduced to a more reasonable price . . . so as to get the Company's compliance to that which is not only fair but just to the town and inhabitants'. By September 1865, a deputation had been formed to negotiate the issue with the Board of Directors.[143] Similar vague charges were brought against the Sligo Gas Company in August 1881. Only in places like Tuam, where the cost of public lighting amounted to £1 per lamp per annum in 1879, [144] did comparative analysis favour the company.

There is little doubt that newspapers were effective in putting comparative analysis before the public. The town commissioners in Newry took over the Gas Company, for £32,000,[145] less than a year after *The Newry Telegraph* drew attention to the acquisition of the gas company by the corporation in Belfast in September 1877, in the following terms:

> Like a great many other towns. . . . Belfast has long complained of the quality of the gas supplied to it by the company having the benefit of a monopoly, and it was thought also that the charge for it was higher than it need have been, though at 3s. 11d. per 1,000 feet the inhabitants of this manufacturing town were paying less than is at the present moment, perhaps, in a majority of boroughs. In spite of a great deal of opportunism and many predictions of failure and mishap, the Town Council of Belfast determined to buy the existing gasworks and carry them on for the benefit of the ratepayers . . . complaints of bad gas seem to have entirely disappeared. The light has been actually improved in quality and satisfaction with it is said to be general. There is no very great alteration in price but an advantage of 2d. per 1,000 ft . . . and a reduction of 50 percent on meter hire is announced. All this is well calculated to encourage the extension of the experiment to other towns affected with bad light and exorbitant charges and it seems very probable that the proper system of supplying our streets and homes with gas will have been attained by the time the universal adoption of the electric light has been rendered practicable.[146]

Consumers had been dissatisfied with gas conditions in Newry since 1869.[147] However, the rashness of this venture was reflected in the simple fact that the town commissioners began to investigate the possibilities of electric lighting only a month after saddling the ratepayers with the cost of the works![148] It is perhaps well to note that it took the corporation in Belfast almost thirty years to acquire the privately owned gas company.[149]

The Journal of Gas Lighting noted that in regard to an unflattering comparison between Dublin and Belfast in 1886, care had to be exercised as, when making sad comparisons, it was 'far easier to blunder than to speak correctly'.[150] Indeed, this had been highlighted in Naas, six years previously, when a detailed comparison between conditions in Naas and those in Omagh, Portadown, Ballymena, Thurles, Nenagh, Banbridge, and Dublin was appreciably undermined by the gas manager's simple but convincing response that the calculations made at the public meeting were entirely erroneous as 'the quality, cost, and carriage of coal . . . are incorrectly given and the towns given for comparison far too north'.[151] There was no denying that 'the Dublin Works supply a district of over 33,000 acres and carbonize 110,000 tons of coal per annum with all the advantages of the best and most approved machinery, the best skilled labour, guided by the highest scientific talent in the Kingdom' or that the extensive manufacturing districts of Omagh, Portadown and Ballymena contained large factories which consumed as much as the entire town of Naas. Gas conditions always looked better from a distance!

In any event, conditions in Newry after 1878 hardly improved under municipal management, and gave resonance to the statement made by H.W. Williams, chairman of the Newry Gas Consumers' Company, in 1877.

> Whenever the subject cropped up at the Commissioners' meetings it was all excitement and strong language – language which was as useless as it was uncalled for. If the members of the municipal body were less eloquent and more practical, and if they would just go with the figures, any man among them of ordinary understanding could see in a few minutes that the Gas Company's offer to them was exceedingly favourable.[152]

Certainly, temperatures rose and 'facts' flew at public meetings on the subject from time to time, especially when private grievances were given a public airing. At Nenagh, in 1860, for instance, one agitator asserted that he had paid as much as Brundley's Hotel for gas on one occasion, though he had but three lights at the time.[153] Nevertheless, opposition was sometimes dignified, as exemplified by the following report of gas proceedings in Carlow, in 1845, by *The Kilkenny Moderator*:

> [At] . . . a numerous and respectable meeting of the inhabitants at the Court House, chaired by T.T. Vigers, Esq., D.C., Mr Edward M. Fitzgerald read communications from Ross, Kilkenny, Clonmel, Waterford, Dundalk, and Armagh related to the price of gas to consumers in the several towns and to the working of gas consumers' companies wherever established. It appeared by the report read from Armagh (where a gas consumer company had been established in 1833) that the shareholders were paid a dividend of 8 percent on their capital, while the committee in their printed report recommend a further reduction in the price of the finest gas in Ireland of 15 percent off 11s. 0d. per 1,000 cubic feet and there remained a surplus profit of £1,800. The meeting was favourable to the establishment of a joint stock company to consist of 400 shares of £5 each and equal of 200 shares were subscribed from in the room. Dr Rawson considered that Mr Colquhoun was entitled to the most favourable consideration, he having built a gasometer, and before any measures were adopted he advised a consultation with that gentleman whose interest could not be fairly overlooked . . . other gentlemen not only agreed with the suggestion but considered the inhabitants bound to make a fair and liberal offer to Mr Colquhoun in the event of a shareholders' company . . . [154]

In that year the Scottish engineer, Mr Colquhoun, had rented a plot of ground on Castle Quay from Samuel Haughton, erected a gasworks and supplied gas to the town at 12s. 6d. per 1,000 cubic feet. With the formation of the Carlow Gaslight Joint Stock Company under the leadership of Simon Clarke, and the erection of a rival works at the end of Montgomery Street, Mr Colquhoun conceded defeat and sold his works for £1,500.[155]

Newspaper reports were often vindictive but were also occasionally restrained in criticism. *The Galway Vindicator and Connaught Advertiser* admitted in March 1859 that 'We have been for some time past hearing many complaints of the indifferent quality of the gas supplied by the local company, and though we have ourselves experienced it and endured its incompetence, we did not complain until now that complaint has become general'.[156] Indeed, a writer to *The Down Recorder* in December 1880 noted that he complained to the paper on several occasions about the quality of gas, but did not hear a word about it through 'the usual good nature' of the responsible parties. Moreover, newspaper men were sometimes almost subtle on the gas question as suggested by *The Londonderry Standard*, noting, in September 1853, that 'As the town of Strabane at present is in the unrivalled position of being well lighted with gas and supplied with water, without costing the inhabitants so much as a single shilling in the year except for the gas consumed by them in the houses and places of business; and as this desirable state of things has been effected by the judicious management of the Town Commissioners who have caused the tools of the market and the property under their control to meet the expenses of the gas lamps and water, a list of the chairmen, each of whom held office for three years, is worthy of being recorded as showing the wisdom of the Commissioners in the election of the Presidents . . . [since] the 29th October 1829'.[157] Clearly, the citizens of Derry had reason to envy those of Strabane where the commissioners had set an example worthy of imitation by every municipal body in Ireland!

Compliments! and Promotion

Journalists were not unknown to flatter and compliment on the slightest pretext. On 9 January 1826 *The Waterford Mirror* reported that the New Waterford Gas Company had commenced lighting the quay and that 'the effect was nearly like that of a public illumination', with no one complaining of an offensive smell. In December 1848 *The Carlow Sentinel* declared 'The charge for . . . gas in the city of London, where coals are sold at 13s. 0d. per ton, is 6s. 0d. per 1,000 cubic feet!! In Carlow and other towns in Ireland, where coals suited for carbonization are seldom less than 23s. 0d. per ton, the charge is but 7s. 0d.!!! See what well directed local enterprise can effect'.[158]

In March 1865 *The Irish Times* remarked favourably on the gas question in Sligo where gas cost 6s. 3d. per 1,000 feet and where the directors were generous enough to donate £50 to the New Town Hall, after declaring a dividend of 8 percent.[159] Gas lighting became a matter of prestige and an indication of urban wealth and sophistication to those which did not possess a works or who wanted better quality gas. In Ballymoney in 1850, for instance, promoters of the proposed gas company were desirous that the town should no longer be deprived of the advantages of gas lighting which had been successfully adopted in Ballymena, Coleraine, Derry, Strabane and many smaller towns of less importance.

Newspaper accounts often helped to promote the industry. As early as February 1816, *The Cork Morning Intelligence* reported that

> The Gas Apparatus fitted up by Mr James O'Brien of Tuckey Street draws every night a crowded assembly of the citizens to witness its effects. The brilliancy of the lamps outside the home, the neatness and novelty with which the shop is lit up, and the extent to which the light is conveyed through his extensive manufactory and work shops have all excited general admiration. We hope to see this improvement generally adopted thro' the city as a remedy to the wretched, expensive mode in which it is now lighted and that every citizen, as in London, will be enabled to take the Gas into his own house at so much per annum. We think that much credit is due to Mr O'Brien for the spirit he has displayed in getting up such an improvement . . . which ere long may be highly useful, generally beneficial and extensively diffused.[160]

In January 1832 *The Wexford Herald* promoted the paving, lighting and cleansing of the streets of Wexford because it 'would impose but a very slight tax upon the prosperity of its citizens'.[161] More than twenty-five years later, *The Dublin Builder* was noting with approval the formation of gasworks at Mullingar, Mountmellick and Tuam, and the installation of private gas plants in counties Wicklow, Monaghan and Tyrone.[162] It was not alone. *The Irish Times*, for instance, noted Sir R.A. O'Donnell's generous efforts to supply Newport with gas in 1860.[163] Indeed, it celebrated a similar 'auspicious event' in Castlederg, on 29 November, as follows:

> The works have been erected by Messrs Edmundson & Co. Dublin at the cost of John G. Smyly Esq, Q.C. the present spirited and generous landlord of the town. On the arrival of Mr Smyly from Dublin, the gas shed forth its brilliant flame to an admiring crowd, composed of townspeople and a large number from the prosperous neighbourhood, many of whom looked upon gas light for the first time with astonishment. . . . During the night, the streets presented a very lively appearance: tar barrels burning; ringing of bells and continuous cheering forming the principal rejoicing of the youthful crowd. Mr Smyly has, with praiseworthy liberality, provided street lamps which are being lighted at his expense . . . [and is] a gentleman who has at heart the welfare of his estate and his tenants, and the prosperity of the country in general.[164]

Clearly, Ireland could do with more of this generosity!

Conservatism and the New Utility

Newspapers frequently confronted conservatism and ignorance, as the following report of a meeting in March 1851 of the Athlone Town Commissioners on the issue of gas lighting shows:

> We have been told, by those who would perpetuate our darkness, that our fathers were wiser and happier and were more prosperous than we are and yet they neither sought after or longed for such novelties. If our love for the memory of dear friends deceased must be tested by plodding through streets in darkness thanking our stars when a propitious luminary sparkles a little more brightly and casts a timely blink on the reservoir of mud to warn us of our danger; or if we must display our attachment by stalking along with a lamp in hand . . . having as much light as renders darkness visible and beguiles poor unsuspecting fellows into some yawning cesspool, we must stand charged and even guilty of the want of filial affection for we have no desire to perpetuate their memory by making such a sacrifice. But we cannot conceive that we are dishonouring their memory or impinging their wisdom when we make a feeble effort to keep pace with the rapid march of intellect by which the century is characterised.[165]

Interestingly enough, it took almost another four years of consideration and discussion before gas lighting was achieved in Athlone!

Opposition to gas lighting was also voiced in other parts of Ireland in the mid-nineteenth century. At Westport, in June 1857, a meeting was called by twenty-two citizens 'to consider the best way to oppose legally, the attempt now about being made, by a few persons, TO LIGHT THE TOWN WITH GAS, in opposition to the wish of the Majority of the Inhabitants'.[166] *The Westmeath Guardian and Longford Newsletter*, of 30 October 1851, commented that:

> The gas-works at the railway station here [Mullingar] are now nearly completed, and we understand that early in the coming week the station will be lighted. A few weeks ago we directed the attention of the shopkeepers of our town to the fact of these works having commenced and pointed out the facility which their erection afforded them for getting their shops lighted; but with one solitary exception, not an individual has stirred in the matter since. True it is that some 'men love darkness rather than light', and evince their ways in more ways than one.[167]

Three weeks earlier, the newspaper had enthused that 'such an opportunity should not be neglected and the inhabitants ought to meet together at once and make a combined effort to effect an object so desirable, when, we doubt not, the directors of the company will act towards them with liberality'.[168] Old ways died hard.

Concerns for Safety

Certainly, there were dangers of gas explosions and gas poisonings, with innocent non-gas consumers sometimes being affected by their neighbour's affinity for gas.[169] Particularly in respect to gas explosions, newspaper accounts seemed to be pointed more in the direction of the sensational aspect than the preventative angle. Apparently, there was nothing remarkable about individuals approaching rooms smelling of gas with naked flames in order to detect gas leakages![170] However, this criticism of newspapers may be a little unfair in that their coverage may have assumed that most people knew how to deal with a leakage of gas. Essentially, the matter was a reasonably simple affair as gas only became explosive when it formed about 10 percent of the atmosphere, and it could be smelt well before that time. As a London gas fitter noted in 1857

> When a leakage is discovered, lights should be kept out of the way, the Gas turned off the main and the doors and upper part of windows should be opened without delay and when the smell of gas is no longer perceived the main tap may be turned on so as to allow a moderate supply, and the fittings followed by a lighted candle or taper commencing at the burner, until the source of escape be found.[171]

Gas explosions resulted from neglect and ignorance for the most part. Even so, responsibility for some explosions was not always easy to pinpoint, as suggested by the report in *The Galway Vindicator* that, on several occasions before searching for a gas leakage with a lighted candle, 'Mr Croker reported what he supposed to be an escape of gas to the officials of the Company, but they informed him that there was no danger and that the smell of a small escape of gas was owing to the inferior quality of coals which they were obliged to consume'. Regarding a terrific gas explosion at the Court House, Green Street, Dublin, in 1867, there was some speculation as to whether the incident was an accident or part of an attempt to free Augustine E. Costello, an alleged Fenian captain.

When a terrible explosion occurred opposite the Salvation Army Barracks in Dungannon, in 1892, a Mr Chapman argued, as reported in *The Tyrone Courier*, 22 October 1892, that 'it was a diabolical attempt of some inscrupulous Tories to upset the present Liberal Government', while John Spence noted that it was 'the effect of the withdrawal of Mr Morley's proclamation and that a lot of dynamite had been sent into town by some Liberals to erect a scare in favour of the government'. However, a Mr

Cassidy was less inclined towards political reasoning in suggesting that 'it is the result of coal gas and sewer gas in their perambulations through the subterranean passage under the town meeting some foul air and pure air mixed and a regular rough and tumble fight taking place between the four Brethren of the infernal regions, and that such a concentration of energy took place, and such a concentrated essence of friction took place to a degree never dreamt of, that an explosion was the result'. He did not blame the gas company but a local grocer who had built a new house on the old sewer and accordingly 'closed up one end of it'.

'Makin' tergates o the gas lamps'

Explosions were not the only focal point for speculation about incidents. In 1891, *The Cork Examiner* reported rumours to the effect that the Roman Catholic Lough Chapel was going to lose its neighbouring lamp stand because some enterprising early-bird had decided to cheat the gas company by re-lighting the lamp after it had been extinguished, and the *Examiner* attributed the motivation for this to the recently proclaimed needs of the Protestant Saint Finbarr's for a new lamp![172]

The newspapers reflected a natural interest in a topic which had its humorous moments. One lady from Summerhill in Cork, for instance, remonstrated regarding the poor lighting of an adjoining street coupled with the tendency of dashing army personnel to entertain young girls there, only to conclude with the somewhat ironic remark that as far as she could see, the situation had not improved with gas lighting![173] In February 1885, *The Drogheda Argus* recorded a lively meeting of the corporation:

> The inspector reported that one of the lamp posts received a compound fracture from Dr Keelan having tried its metal by running his trap against it. He left it stretched on the roadway. Another of the lamp posts was floored by Mr Galbraith's bread cart following the example of the medical faculty. Capt. Branigan [said] 'It is the least the doctor should have done, to pull up and put a plaster on it'.[174]

Authorities elsewhere took a less tolerant view of the unnecessary suffering of lamp posts. In September 1905 *The Coleraine Chronicle* included the following letter.

> I hev been readin' in the Chronicle that the boys are makin' tergates o the gas lamps in the town, and I'm fairly fritened out o my wits at the manner that the Council is goin' to take to ketch the offenders, who are already beginnin' to larn how to shoot, so that they be ready when the volunteers are called up for trainin'. I'm onlucky enuff to live near a lamp post and I'm wonderin how I am to ketch the chap that manes to brek this lamp some nicht. Me and the missus

hev our work to do in the day times and if we set up to watch we may drop asleep near the mornin' and not hear the horn when it sounds to wake the people up and then maybe we'll lose half a day and we are too poor to pay this much for watchin' gas lamps. Then if we have the childer to watch, the poor things may ketch a could instead of catchen the glass breaker and then mebbe we might all heve measles or influensa. I wondher with all the wisdom of J.P.'s and x-chairmen to sey nothin o vestrymen and merchants that they could no invent a better plan than this.[175]

There was obviously more to gas lighting than simple questions of cost and quality. Indeed, some urban centres were governed by 'the moon cyle'. Cork was one such city to economise on gas by availing of moonlight, and the corporation's failure to take proper care in studying astronomical forecasts was registered, in November 1891, by *The Cork Examiner*.[176] Little more than two years earlier, *The Journal of Gas Lighting*, in defending Dublin from misers, had expressed the following view:

Now, although the moon schedule may work fairly well in quiet rural localities where everybody is supposed to be indoors, if not in bed, by ten, it is scarcely sufficient for the city of Dublin. Naturally, peaceful, sober, and law-abiding, as we have lately learnt to regard the Irish nation on the whole, their best friends must admit that there are a few black sheep among them – of foreign origin, mayhap, – who are not above taking advantages of a dark night for the perpetration of mischief not always harmless.[177]

By inference, the quality of a locality could be discerned from the mode of lighting in operation!

Edification

Newspapers also assumed an educational function and displayed an extensive range of material on the subject of gas. In August 1847 *The Kilkenny Journal* brought the attention of its readers to the discovery of a natural gas jet at Wigmore in Hertfordshire about twelve months before, and to the fact that 'the gas is very pure, quite free from any offensive smell and does not stain the ceilings as is generally the case with the manufactured article'.[178] In November 1856 *The Cork Examiner* lauded the arrangement at Athy gasworks, 'suggested by Professor Sullivan of this city', whereby peat was burned to produce gas to fuel the retorts, while touching upon the more recent innovations of R.L. Johnson.[179] In February 1863 *The Irish Times* welcomed the introduction of gas lighting into the carriages of the Ulster Railway Line, and explained how the process worked in order to encourage other railway companies to adopt a better and less expensive fuel than oil.[180]

Though not as optimistic, in June 1864 *The Dublin Builder* elaborated as follows

> An apparatus has been recently patented . . . for supplying gas to railway carriages in such a manner that the gas may be compressed and admitted into the apparatus at a high pressure, and so regulated as to be consumed at the burners at a low . . . pressure, so that each carriage may carry a comparatively large quantity of gas. For this purpose they fix to the top of the carriage a pipe or series of pipes which act as a holder or reservoir of high pressure gas, and from these pipes the gas, having its passage controlled by a valve, is carried through a regulator to the burners, before arriving at which it passes through a chamber in which it is suffered to expand, thus reducing the pressure . . . [181]

On 10 January 1885 *The Donegal Independent* brought its readers' attention to the operation of a new gas burner from which the light of one hundred candles could be obtained for somewhat less than 1d. per hour, with the view that this 'would appear to render it difficult for the electric or any other light to successfully compete with the new development of successfully burning gas.'

On occasion, newspapers highlighted the legal aspects of consumer-company relations as 'vestries, local boards and public companies are difficult bodies to make an impression on'.[182] There is little doubt but that this was effective. For instance, in May 1885, upon discovering that the Queenstown Gas Company had been compelled by law to furnish detailed accounts, Alderman Smith complained of the very meagre information he received from Waterford Corporation with respect to the gas account and thereby started an investigation into the question.[183] However, newspapers were not unknown to support gas manufacturers as suggested by the provision of hints for the economical use of gas by *The Larne Observer* in August 1906.[184] Here, the underlying assumption was that consumer neglect was often responsible for poor quality gas, an idea often favoured by gas companies.

Certainly, all public condemnation of gas companies was not justified. In his memoirs, Henry Still, manager of Cork Gasworks, recalled taking Dr Power and the guardians of the lunatic asylum to task in 1861 for complaining to *The Cork Examiner* about the poor quality of gas when filth, and not gas, was at fault.[185] Newspapers did not always check or reject such negative information. The minutes of the Dundalk Gas Company, for instance, contain the following entry on 11 November 1859.

> An article having appeared in a local paper, *Newry Examiner*, on Wednesday 9th last setting forth that a Bonfire had been made in the evening of the 5th inst at the works for the purpose of insulting the Roman Catholic inhabitants of the

town. Upon investigating the affair it appeared from the manager's statement, corroborated by the five men that the fire in question was the act of Mr Shimeld's children, assisted by a son of Mr Peter Good, firing a few shavings . . . the Directors regret a Public Journal should give insertion to such an article without at first making enquiries as to the origin of it.[186]

There was even a letter published in *The Cork Examiner* in January 1893 complaining of the quality of gas lighting in Green Street by a phantom Francis Maguire from a non-existent address at 11 Westview, Pouladuff.[187] However, authentic complaints were no laughing matter and could lead to lightning suspensions, embarrassing demotions, or sizable fines. For instance, lamplighters in Cork were not normally given the benefit of too many warnings on the merits of sobriety, punctuality and efficiency.[188] Labour relations favoured management during the nineteenth century and only slowly changed with the decline of the manufacturing industry through international, technological and political developments during the twentieth century.

The Dublin Alliance and Consumers Gas Company was renowned for its unusual and interesting displays. This display is from the 1940s at the Royal Dublin Society Show.

Gas in the bathroom! 'All the hot water you require on bath night for a few pence'. Another display from the Dublin Gas Company.

This display from Dublin Gas shows the use of gas for water-heating outside the home. This display is from the 1930s.

Gas heating in a restaurant of the 1930s, as suggested by Dublin Gas.

Dublin Gas supplied not only gas but also coke. Thus cooking needs and heating needs could be supplied by the company. Again from the 1930s, the 'ideal' kitchen, both warm and efficient.

Chapter 3

Life at the Gasworks

LABOUR RELATIONS

The importance of gas production, distribution and use and its impact on urban life was demonstrated early in the twentieth century with the second gas workers' strike in Cork. It began on 16 May 1901 when, as the company minutes record: 'Four men in the new retort house refused to charge retorts as required by the manager. They were ordered out of the retort house and four men from the yard brought in and they did the work. All the stokers and yardmen then left work. The manager sent for the secretary, and when he and Mr Harrington tried to reason with the men, pointing out the consequences of their action, their reply was that they would not return to work until the four men were reinstated and they left the works in a body at about 5.30 p.m.'[1] Accordingly, the gas supply failed at about 9.30 p.m. the following night, leaving the city in complete darkness except for that portion covered by electric light.[2]

By 20 May, *The Cork Examiner* concluded that 'a more serious strike has not occurred for many years'.[3] Delays were experienced at the Despatch and Telegraph Department of the Post Office while manufacturing establishments dependent on gas engines were brought to a standstill. The *Examiner* predicted the possible loss of a thousand jobs outside of the gas industry, noting the particular difficulties encountered by bakers, butchers, restaurant owners, hospital catering staff, typesetters and tram-conductors, and condemning increased charges for coal and oil.[4] There is little doubt that all sectors of the community felt the ill-effects of the strike as gas was the main medium for lighting and cooking. Even transportation by sea was affected, with three captains patiently waiting for Parnell Bridge to be opened, by gas, to allow them an exit from the city to the sea. Indeed, but for the advice of D. O'Connell, a plumber from Paul Street, and the resultant utilisation of blow lamps in the offices of *The Cork Examiner*, the event might have escaped coverage without the gas required to melt the lead on the linotypes.[5]

This strike lasted a few months, unlike a previous strike in February 1901. That first strike was settled after a few days, with company directors considering the laborious nature of the work and the fact that 'the men were so good and willing to work'.[6] They overlooked the personal animosity between the stokers and the manager, J. McGrath. On that occasion, the men maintained that they were ordered in an unfair and unjustifiable manner'.[7] Apparently McGrath was a strict disciplinarian, for 'if one of them came only a quarter of an hour late to his morning work he was sent away till noon time when he might resume work, with his wages docked a half-day', and if this occurred twice in the same week 'the employee might be dismissed'.[8] In any case, three stokers who had disobeyed the manager had been reinstated after the February strike on condition that, in the event of a future strike by the men, adequate notice would be given to management.[9] As a result of a similar event only three months later when the men failed to provide such notice, it was hardly surprising that the directors refused to appease the men and further undermine the authority of their manager. For their part, the men argued that

> There was an agreement drawn up between Mr Travers and the men to work No. 4 Retort House, each man to carbonize 2 tons, 3 cwt of coal thus making 10 tons 12 cwt for a gang of four men. Everything worked satisfactorily until Mr McGrath took over the management, when he wanted the men to break the contract and burn more coal. The manager said that we were not carbonizing our usual complement of coal and we maintain we are burning over our coal. As an instance, a man is employed to wheel coal from one side of the house to the other side, and he very often has to wheel 118 barrows of coal, with 2 cwt on each barrow, when his complement is 106 barrows. On Thursday evening, the manager ordered the men to charge the retorts according to the heats. The men said they would put the usual charge in them. He told them that they should do whatever they were told, but if we burned extra coal we would deprive other men of earning a livelihood. The manager asked each man individually to burn extra coal which the men declined to do, and they were instantly dismissed.[10]

This statement by James Gorman, secretary of the Cork Gas Workers' Society, was rejected by the company. With the help of blackleg labourers from Wexford, Dublin and Mallow,[11] they managed to provide a reasonable supply of gas by early June.[12] It was September, however, before life at the gasworks began to return to normal, with most of the strikers accepting company dictates.[13] By then *The Cork Examiner* had long lost interest in the question, as the vulnerability of the city rather than the obstinacy of the men had clearly been the main ingredient of its multi-sided coverage.

The Belfast Corporation Gasworks and offices in Ormeau Road, circa 1923.

General view of the coke telpherage system and vertical retort plant in Belfast Gasworks, circa 1923.

MANAGEMENT – STRICT ECONOMY AND A WATCHFUL EYE

The strike highlighted the working environment and general orientation of the gas company. In spite of the sporadic advances of electricity, the disorganised demands of labour, the considerable inconvenience felt by all consumers, and an overdraft of more than ten thousand pounds,[14] it did not feel sufficiently threatened to concede worker demands. At the time management was supreme and the work-force generally loyal, as suggested by the lack of violence during the strike and the willingness of the strikers to prevent a second major explosion at the works through the ignorance of the new men.[15] Indeed, until 1901, only an odd case of injury, embezzlement, incompetence or petty disagreement had marred a working environment which had demanded diligence, loyalty and honesty since the company's foundation in 1856.

This is demonstrated in the company's minutes. In August 1861, a Mr Evans was encouraged to resign the secretaryship of the Waterford Gas Company in order to continue his work as accountant in Cork.[16] Likewise, in April 1862 it was felt that the collector, a Mr Barry, could not afford the time from company business which would allow him the opportunity to act as accountant for the Queenstown Gas Company.[17] When John Lyne left the company in February 1862, to become manager of the Youghal Gas Works, he was not replaced as it was thought advisable to allocate his former duties (without any mention of extra pay) to the public inspector of meters and other servants of the company.[18] When a Mr Francis made an error in paying wages in November 1862, the specified amount was taken from his wages in weekly instalments of five shillings.[19] Clearly, the company functioned in accordance with a strict economy, under the watchful eye of its directors and staff, and upon the principle of company before individual.

Naturally enough, this was not always an easy code to work under. In December 1861, for instance, the inspector of public lamps, John Bennett, was reprimanded for not reporting one of the lamplighters for drunkenness, and warned that a similar occurrence in the future would lead to his dismissal.[20] Likewise, in April 1863 an investigation was initiated to discern why Denny Lane had to dismiss a night foreman who had been intoxicated and violent while on duty. This incident had been reported to Mr Travers who had assumed the manager's responsibilities during the absence of Henry Still.[21]

As suggested by 'the 1867 lime affair', the company also operated with a view to maintaining an adequate chain of command. The lime affair, involving Henry Still, is recorded in the company minutes of 20 July as follows.

The retort house in Newtownards, Co. Down, described at the time (1946) as 'an imposing building on modern lines'.

Mr Still complained of very violent language used towards him by F. McCarthy and a letter was read from the latter stating that at one period Mr Still had charged the Company 10d. per barrel for some lime when he had himself paid only 6d. per barrel for it. Mr F. McCarthy, Coke Clerk, attended the Board and stated that in the year 1861 Mr Still had charged the Company with 10d. per barrel for 72 barrels of lime and that he had paid the late Mr Daly only 6d. per barrel for the same. It appeared that at the period in question, Mr McCarthy had paid several small accounts for Mr Still and he produced Mr Daly's account furnishment at 6d. per barrel and paid by him. He being asked why he had not sooner called attention to the matter, he said he had mislaid the bill but that he had mentioned the matter to the store-keeper whose business it was to mention it to the Secretary. J. Mahony was called in and stated that he had at the time mentioned it in the office either to the Secretary or to Mr Evans the accountant. The Secretary said that he had no recollection whatever of the matter and on referring to the petty-ledger of the period a memorandum in Mr Evans's handwriting was found referring to 112 barrels delivered by W. Daly immediately after it 6 but credited to Mr Still at 10d.[22]

The situation obviously did not favour Mr Still. Nevertheless, the issue took on a different complexion on 22 July when Mr Still attended the board of directors. He conceded that there was little doubting the facts, while wondering how lime could be supplied for 6d. per barrel when the usual price was 4s. 2d. Upon hearing this, J. Mahony, the store-keeper, stated that the lime was slick, only to be severely reprimanded for witholding this information from Mr Still earlier in the day and 'thereby depriving him of the opportunity of investigating the charges'.[23] The directors also reprimanded Mr McCarthy for insolence of manner towards Mr Still, 'although they did not blame McCarthy for bringing the matter forward'.[24] They thought that there had been some slight irregularity, but concluded 'that there was no error committed by Mr Still'.[25]

Certainly, this question of no more than £1 4s. 0d. was hardly comparable with a Mr Forde's fraudulent appropriation of coke in November 1860,[26] the forging of Denny Lane's signature on a bill for £720 by a Mr Harns in August 1868,[27] or the embezzlement of £1,000 by a Mr Collins in 1872.[28] However, Mr Still did not escape being reprimanded. This is suggested by the fact that, in October 1871, 'the Directors expressed very strong condemnation of Mr Still for not having met Mr Anderson, stating that it was the duty of the officers of the company to confer together upon subjects of interest to the company and that no personal feeling should prevent them from meeting.[29] With regard to the lime affair, or more specifically complaints from subordinates, the directors preferred not to interfere in the details of management where possible.[30]

THE CONTRIBUTION
OF ALFRED HENRY STILL

There is reason to suspect that Alfred Henry Still was not the easiest man to work with or under. In October 1861, for instance, the lamplighters turned down an advance in weekly wages, from 12s. 0d to 14s. 0d., because of the stipulation that they should then give Mr Still the extra time he required.[31] In April 1866, a fitter named Edward Sexton complained of ill-treatment by Mr Still to the directors and 'asserted that he had been dismissed from the company's employment without cause and another person put in his place, and that Mr Still refused to give him a letter testifying to his abilities as a workman and good conduct to which he said he was entitled'.[32] Indeed, the company minutes for the years 1871 and 1872 record instances of disagreement between Mr Still and Messrs Lane, Collins and Bennett.[33]

Still also got on poorly with the consulting engineer, George Anderson, whose opinion he thought worthless and whose integrity he questioned because Anderson had apparently sold a tar process to Dublin Gas which he had seen in Cork and which Still himself and Denny Lane had patented.[34] Still was also known to over-work.[35]

In spite of the many disagreements, the initial success of the consumer company was largely due to the efforts of Henry Still. Throughout 1857 he consistently rose at 5 a.m. to keep teams of men working on the new distribution network. With the help of 'torch boys', he worked until late at night in order to meet the corporation deadline and surpass even the directors' expectations.[36] Before coming to Cork upon a year's contract, Still had gained considerable knowledge and skill working in London's various gasworks since 1835 and had made certain innovations in regard to the clearance of naphthaline in pipes and the removal of ammonia in gas.[37] His arrival in Cork may have had something to do with a variety of factors: the religious bigotry in London after his conversion to Catholicism; his friendship with J.J. Murphy from Ringmahon Castle, Blackrock; or his observation that 'firemen and stokers from Ireland were superior to the English for such trying work' and were liable 'to take a draught of Porter – one quart right off' when 'in a state of profuse perspiration'.[38] In any case, Henry Still had been approached in London by J.F. Maguire and by Denny Lane in August 1857 on the recommendation of George Anderson.[39] He proved himself capable of running, amalgamating and developing both gasworks in Cork upon the defeat of the United General Gas Company in 1859.

Clearly, Still's achievement was greatly appreciated. In September 1893, it was resolved 'that Mr Still be given a retiring allowance of £200 per annum, payable monthly, subject to review at any time that, in the opinion of the Directors, the circumstances of the Company should require it', and 'that he also be given the continued use of his house as Caretaker for the Company with a reasonable allowance of coal and gas'.[40] The fact that he remained in Cork for almost forty-four years suggests he loved working there, as he would have had little difficulty securing work elsewhere, being highly regarded as consultant engineer in Limerick, Queenstown, Dungarvan, Youghal, Killarney, Bandon, Midleton and Fermoy.[41] Certainly he encountered unforeseen difficulties as manager in Cork. In March 1858, for instance, after he had expended considerable time and energy in combating serious gas leakages, it was discovered that 'Ashlin, Field, and Callaghan . . . had been engaged in a system of gross deception . . . so as to make it appear that the leakage had been materially diminished when in fact it had not been so. They had ingeniously placed a bladder in several mains at a short distance from the meter which was employed for the purpose of testing the sturdiness of the mains. By this means, they cut off all communication with the greater part of the system of pipes under test, no leakage beyond the bladder giving any indication in the meter'.[42]

THE FATE OF OTHER MANAGERS

Other managers were not so fortunate. In January 1892 Mr Cronin, manager of the Corporation Gas Works in Bandon, addressed his elected superiors as follows:

Mr Chairman and Gentlemen – In order to make your works pay, and to keep the machinery in proper order, I would suggest that you would place, by resolution, your manager in his proper position. Also to allow him a free hand in propagating the use of gas for cooking and heating. . . . By instructing the consumers in the use of lighting, cooking and heating by gas the quantity would be increased by distribution; the plant could be utilized by day as well as by night, leakage would be diminished.[43]

No immediate action was taken, although this report concluded by stating that more coal was required. In Dundalk, little notice was taken of G.R. Love's desire for the formulation of a rigid code of conduct for employees with regard to drinking in particular, or of his warnings about gas explosions should the town commissioners proceed with their plan to use a steam roller over gas mains![44] In 1870, serious consideration was given to the question of whether or not the gas manager in Ballinasloe should handle the sale of residuals and the finances there entailed![45] In 1887, Athlone's responsible town board did not get too excited when

> The manager stated that at present he was so busy with the purifiers he could not attend [the lamps]. The lime he had to use was so bad that he kept two men constantly engaged with the purifier. He should get help to look after the outside works, for he was himself continuously working like any of the men in the yard and had not a moment scarcely to eat his food.[46]

In 1901, Alderman Morrissey of Clonmel refused to pay the manager for gas consumed,[47] and his 'disputed bill' went unnoticed until he lost his foothold in the Corporation! Indeed, in 1918, Wexford's company directors succeeded in suspending and dismissing their new secretary and manager, A. Lyne, after attempting to avert a strike at the works.[48]

CONFLICT BETWEEN
MANAGEMENT AND DIRECTORS

This event was particularly curious given the long association of the Lyne family with the company. It attracted considerable publicity and a shareholders' meeting was subsequently called to dismiss one or more directors. Wexford Gas Consumers' Company was formed in April 1865, after more than a hundred citizens asked Mayor John Walsh to call a public meeting on the issue. This took place before James Furness, the then-bankrupt gas trader, facilitated the purchase of the Wexford and Ross gas works for £3,000, less than half its value.[49]

John Pitt was appointed manager of the Wexford Gas Works and secretary to the company at a salary of £150 per year in June 1865. He was also to receive £150 for managing the Ross works until it was found in October 1865 that he was not competent to fulfil all his duties.[50] Mr Pitt had given much time to the financial affairs of the company. He argued that he was wrongfully dismissed and thereby secured £150 'in full satisfaction of his claims'.[51] John Lyne, who had worked under Henry Still in Cork between 1858 and 1862, took his place as manager and secretary of the Wexford company at a reduced salary of £90 per annum with a free house, supply of gas and an allowance of £4 per year for coal.[52]

With the sale of the Ross works, and the capable management and innovations of John Lyne, the company prospered without major labour or other difficulties. There were the usual minor problems related to drink or embezzlement, disagreements with the corporation and complaints related to the quality of gas. However, the directors placed their confidence in John Lyne's judgement; they were satisfied that the illuminating power of the light was equal to, if not better than, that supplied by the former

The operating stage of the Belfast water-gas plant, circa 1923.

Livesey washers used in the gas purification process for tar removal, Belfast circa 1923.

contractor.[53] The directors even decided that no notice should be taken of anonymous complaints in newspapers or complaints made outside the company's office.[54] With the death of John Lyne on 13 July 1918, the company showed its appreciation of his labours by conceding Mrs Lyne's request that her son Alfred, the then assistant manager, be appointed manager and secretary in his father's place.[55]

Apparently this decision was not taken lightly. In July 1918, the following was proposed by Mr Walsh and passed unanimously by the Board of Directors.

> That the new Engineer, General Manager and Secretary must consider it his duty to bring all business matters before the Directors at the weekly meeting, all letters, orders and correspondence of every kind to be placed on the table at each weekly meeting and no letters of extra importance are to be sent out without having been first approved by Directors. That the accounts books *viz* sale books, wages books, and ledgers to be placed on the table at all meetings of the Directors. The books to be properly written up and reported into the ledger up to the day of each meeting.[56]

This firm resolution, made prior to the appointment of the new manager and secretary, may have had something to do with the fact that the younger Mr Lyne, as shareholder of the company, had objected to a proposed increase in the directors' fees some years before.[57] It may equally have arisen from a natural tendency of the directors to assert themselves when given the opportunity. In any case, the new arrangement was not destined to last. On 29 October 1919, Alfred Lyne produced a letter from a Mr Corish stating that the men would be called out on Tuesday 29 October if their demands were not granted. Lyne assured the directors that the men's demand for an eight-hour shift was unworkable and that he could handle the matter.[58] He then offered the men the opportunity to come to work at 7 a.m., to have forty-five minutes for breakfast and an hour for dinner before departing at 6 p.m. (yardmen) or 6 .30 p.m. (foremen).[59]

When the men turned down this arrangement by walking out, the directors became unduly anxious about their legal obligations to supply gas. After a number of meetings, which gave an airing to the shareholders' ideas about the verification of any settlement, the directors unwisely agreed to the gas inspector's suggestion that the men resume work on their own terms without prejudice to the final settlement resulting from a shareholders' meeting.[60] By shifting the legal situation from one of a strike to a potential lockout, and by practically conceding the workers' demands at a stroke, the directors informed their manager that the issue had been settled. When Lyne refused to resume work without the 'agreed' shareholders' meeting, the directors naturally suspended him. He obligingly tendered his resignation –

then changed his mind. He subsequently declined the resultant offer that he become manager only and succeeded in convincing other relevant parties of the need for a shareholders' meeting. The directors had little intention of being dictated to by a manager overtaken with his status as shareholder. So they immediately appointed the then manager of Midleton Gas Works, R.F. McCroy, as their new manager and secretary. The fact that McCroy later declined the honour hardly mattered. At the shareholders' meeting in January 1919 Alfred Lyne lost his motion to investigate the context of his grievances. In all, 572 voted against the proposed dismissal of the directors, 284 voted in favour and 111 votes were uncast. Clearly, the majority of impartial stockholders were opposed to the former manager, especially since 101 votes were held by the Lyne family.[61]

MANAGERIAL APPOINTMENTS

The removal of other managers did not attract such negative publicity. In Dundalk, for instance, dismissal was achieved with a certain mixture of stealth and financial wisdom as suggested by the treatment of Messrs Clarke, Dyer, Shimeld and Featherstone. In July 1856, an investigation was initiated following charges by Messrs Connolly and Nicholson that Dundalk's manager, John Clarke, had given coal to James Dillon in direct violation of company decree.[62] Only when Charles Dyer accepted the position of manager on 8 August was Mr Clarke informed that his services would not be required after 15 August when he was paid a gratuity of £36 'upon leaving his premises'.[63] Undue interference by the directors in management led to Dyer tendering his resignation before the end of 1856, but he subsequently withdrew this. The directors, however, refused to accept his change of heart.[64] A Mr Shimeld of Leeds was recommended for the job. Shimeld was willing to manage the works for £80 per annum with free apartments, coal and gas; Dyer had been promised £150 a year with free house, coal and gas; Dyer had been promised £150 a year with free house, coal and gas, along with a share in the profits in excess of £330.[65]

In 1886, Mr Shimeld's inability to impress the accountant led to his own dismissal. The directors made another small profit when W.B. Featherstone, assistant at Scarborough Gas Works, agreed to do the job for £30 less than Shimeld,[66] at least initially.[67] Unfortunately, Featherstone was dismissed in 1891, as the company did not appreciate having to pay £6 5s. 0d. to the Dundalk Athletic Club through their manager's generosity.[68] Featherstone's removal was facilitated with the promise of three months' pay upon departure.[69] Other authorities were not as decisive. In August 1908, for instance, the question of 'alleged removals' by an employee of the gasworks divided the Newry Gas Committee, with the effect that it was the butt of local jest for some time afterwards.

Managers came and went for various reasons, some of which were recorded. In Dungannon, for instance, Charles Reilly was dismissed in 1869 for 'dereliction of duty' and failed in his attempt to be reappointed despite popular local opinion in his favour.[70] His successor, James Micklyohn, resigned in 1872 on becoming manager of Portadown gasworks.[71] Robert Green was appointed in his place but wanted £100 per annum instead of the £90 offered and was accordingly replaced by a Mr Evans.[72] In 1882, Mr Robert Montgomery had to resign his position as manager due to the poor financial record shown that year. He was succeeded by a Mr Ross who evidently pleased the relevant authorities as he was awarded various bonuses and his salary was raised from £100 to £120 within three years of his appointment.[73]

Obviously, the right man for the job was not always easy to find. In Carrickfergus, after employing two managers – Andrew Todd and E.H. Osborne – in as many years, the directors advertised for 'a practical manager' in 1895.[74] As a result, they secured the able services of Robert Campbell at £80 per annum. They recognised his ability by raising his salary to £90 in 1896, £100 in 1897, £120 in 1909 and £135 in 1911.[75] Campbell was clearly quite shrewd, as is suggested by his successful application for the job of secretary in 1909. In recommending himself for this position, Campbell stated that, unlike other gas managers, he had done work beyond the call of duty in operating as a gas fitter without personal gain, he had rejected a job offer which paid £20 more than his current wage with the expectation of securing the secretaryship, he had a competent fifteen-year-old daughter training in administration whom he was willing to put in the office so that it could remain open all day and the manager acted as secretary in twenty-one works in Ireland.[76]

Others were not as lucky as Campbell, or perhaps as able. When R.P. Bullock, manager at Donaghadee, asked for a raise in September 1863, his basic salary being £40 a year, it was two months before he was given an assistant to lighten his work load.[77] His immediate successor, A. Thomas Mark, was also paid £40 on his appointment in January 1865 until his resignation in December 1866, when Mr Bullock was reappointed with a salary of £52.[78] Even after the appointment of three further managers between 1871 and 1898 – Messrs Park, Haken and Coulter – James Worth's starting salary as manager was no more than £65 per annum at the turn of the century.[79]

Finances were obviously tight at Donaghadee, as company secretaries fared even worse than the managers. In 1865, Hugh Nowell's application for an increase on £20 a year was rejected and the directors saw fit to place only a single advertisement for a replacement upon his resultant resignation.[80] When Nowell's successor resigned in 1879, a Mr Lendson secured the secretaryship at £12 a year![81]

Falling salary scales on appointments were not peculiar to Donaghadee. With the appointment of James Hutchinson in Portrush in 1877, the current rate for managerial service dived from £90 to £75.[82] Blissfully unaware of the drop, Mr Hutchinson asked for a raise in April 1879, resigned in September of the same year, and reapplied for his former job later that month. Apparently, his services were not fully appreciated by all members of the board; he was informed that he would only be taken back as manager on condition that he apologise to the secretary for abusive language and pay for the advertisements necessitated by his imminent departure![83] When he refused to do either, they appointed William Thompson manager at 25 shillings a week.[84] When Thompson quit after a fortnight, a Mr Leahy was employed at £85 a year, tendering his resignation within two years on demand of £100 a year.[85] In fairness to the company in question, the manager was free to supplement his income through operating as a gas fitter. This was also the case in Larne until 1866 when the directors decreed – after their attention had been repeatedly called to the manager's absence from the works – that Peter McGregor 'shall not engage in any work or works outside of the boundary of the town unless by permission of the directors so that as much of his time as possible shall be devoted to the business of the company'.[86] In 1870, McGregor retaliated, in veiled terms, by asking for an increase in pay because of the devaluation in currency during the nineteen years of his service to the company, the quadrupling of business since then and the comparative rates of pay in other works. McGregor also pointed to the fact that

> I was able to augment my salary to some extent by supplying new fittings and introducing the gas into houses. But most people being now supplied there is little of this required except trifling repairs not very remunerative. Most of you are aware that I save the company a very considerable amount yearly in setting my own retorts, repairing old meters and making all the necessary repairs connected with the works, all of which other companies have to pay for.[87]

In light of McGregor's past services and the fact that Ballymena paid their manager £110 per annum, Carrickfergus £85 and Antrim £75 (with an acre and a half of orchard),[88] his salary was raised from £70 to £85.

Qualifications for Managers

Performance obviously varied from place to place as did expectations about managerial responsibilities and qualifications. In January 1881, following the death of Mr Ryan, the gas manager in Cashel, various gas managers were asked what they considered the necessary qualifications for Ryan's successor should be.[89] Mr Spillane, manager of Limerick Gasworks, stated that 'a great deal depended on the capacity of one to profit by his experience, three years' service ought to be sufficient; it is a matter of opinion and there could be no fixed rule on the subject'. Apparently, Spillane's opinion was not too far off the mark as estimations of requirements varied from two to seven years' experience, while it was noted that Spillane himself had not even three months' experience before becoming manager at Limerick! On the recommendation of Mr Anderson, and with a month's practical experience, a Mr Maloney was appointed manager over Cashel works which badly needed a new gasholder, a tar tank, new retorts, furnace doors and pressure gauges![90] Cashel's directors seemed to agree on one point: 'that no one should be appointed except a respectable man – no one should be appointed on the grounds that he was cheap . . . as a respectable man would prove cheapest in the end'.[91] This was the official reply to patrick Storan's application for the job which had been published in *The Cashel Gazette*:

> Permit me, through your columns, to inform the gentlemen of the Town Council that I'm a candidate for the management of the Gas Works. Taking into consideration the residence on the premises with a garden attached; also the most important fact that of not being under any master except the Town Commissioners; I am prepared to give solvent security for the diligent and competent discharge of all the duties appertaining to the position at £52 a year, my present salary. Being a competent gas fitter, I shall require no second assistant which will be a saving of £80 a year in the management of the gas works. I may mention that I could not hereafter take a second assistant as all such appointments rest with the Town Commissioners. I can produce most respectable testimonials as to my competency both as gas manager and fitter, as during the late Mr Ryan's illness and since his death the entire management has devolved on me. I can with confidence appeal to the gas consumers as to the manner I discharged my duty.[92]

Apparently, the place had been turned into 'a regular dancing school' under Storan's management![93] In any case, the appointment of managers could clearly be an emotive issue. Popular local opinion in Clonmel even as late as 1951, for instance, promoted and defended family tradition and thereby ensured the continuance of 'Kneeshaw management' in direct opposition to a corporation appointment.[94] In Strabane, Charles Hert of Westminster was appointed manager of the new works in 1902. This led one prejudiced party to point to 'the great outcry raised at the present time to stop emigration' and to the danger that 'in fifty years hence the Celt will be outnumbered in his own country', before giving vent to the following:

Are there no competent engineers in Ireland to satisfy the local magnates? Is there no intellect so mighty to devise and plan a gasworks for a small town of 5,000? Land of Burke and Sheridan, Fox, Grattan and O'Connell. Town of Sigerson, Collins and Dunlop. You have indeed fallen on evil times. Acknowledge the superiority of the Great Imperial races. You lead the way, let others follow, forget the past. Hurrah for England! Rule Britannia.[95]

Evidently, the job was too good to give an Englishman!

Clearly, the positon of gas manager was worth having. In Downpatrick, Charles Mearns, had succeeded his own father as manager and stated that the job should go to his son Stanley upon his retirement. However, the directors did not feel altogether safe with Stanley, even with his father's willingness to remain as adviser.[96] Accordingly, they kept old Mearns relatively content with salary increases and various bonuses until the elder Mearns insisted that he was unfit for the work. The directors then appointed a fellow called Quigley from Antrim for a probationary period. They refused to humour Charles Mearns in his desire to return although 'he knew all about the place' and complained that 'he had been very poorly treated after all these years of service'.[97] Quigley could not find any tools at the works, proved to be 'altogether incompetent' even when he had them, and was paid off before his time of probation expired. Meanwhile, Charles Mearns applied for a pension but failed to obtain it when the new manager, Mr Anderson, exposed the poor conditions existing in the works. Apparently, it was not unusual for new candidates to highlight the shortcomings of the old in an effort to win favour.

The Tuam Herald took obvious delight in unearthing a difference of opinion between the new and the old managers in Tuam in 1890.

Is the town hall to be blown into atoms? Forbid to Heaven! But, on last Monday, at the meeting of the Fathers of the City, the Tuam Gas Manager threw a literary bombshell into the very midst of these placid gentlemen which placed utter confusion and dismay in their gentle and unexpectant breasts. This epistolary missile . . . that the gas pipes at the top of the city are liable of such diabolical contrivance that at any time . . . an explosion might take place and tear half the city apart and everybody beneath the roof even blown in a thousand fragments over an astonished and awe stricken world. . . . We admire the courage of this select bank of heroes who instead of then and there scampering in scared fashion homewards calmly continued to discuss the matter and ultimately decided to call in an expert to decide between the literary bomb thrower and the former occupant of the post who strongly asserted that there was no danger whatever and that the Commissioners could lay their heads peacefully upon their pillows.[98]

Belfast Gasworks in the 1930s, seen from the river Blackstaff with the waterless gasholder in the background.

Certainly, standards varied. In 1899 in Newbridge, the laziness of the gas manager was highlighted with the observation that he had not even bothered to re-erect lamp posts which had been knocked down years before.[99] On the other hand, the manager at Enniskillen, Mr Arthur Dimbleby, was warmly recognised as active, obliging and intelligent in 1866.[100]

Duties of Management

In Larne, the regulations governing the duties of both manager and secretary were simply tabulated in 1851.

1. No admittance except on business.

2. The Manager to lock the gate every night himself after seeing all right, and to open the gate in the morning. The key of the gate to be kept by him.

3. The retorts to be charged as follows: 6 o'clock morning, 10 o'clock forenoon, 4 o'clock evening and 9½ o'clock evening. On leaving in the evening the furnace to be well fed and raked and the damper to be near closed.

4. The coals to be weighed into the retorts and the indications to be taken before the drawing of the retorts.

5. A pressure to be left up during the day of at least 3/10 inch and at night till 10 o'clock, 1 inch.

6. The lamps to be lighted and extinguished as follows during the month of September lighted at 8 pm, extinguished at 5 am.

October	6 pm,	6 am.
November	5 pm,	6 am.
December	5 pm,	7 am.
January	5 pm,	6 am.
February	6 pm,	6 am.
March	7 pm,	5 am.
April	8 pm,	4 am.

The manager to see every lamp within one hour after lighting and if any one be not burning right to rectify it immediately. Each lamp to be cleaned once in five days or three times in a fortnight or oftener if required.

7. Each meter to be examined once a month, the indication to be taken and the water line to be corrected.

8. The accounts to be made out and collected quarterly.

9. An account to be kept of all expenditure whether by workmen's wages or goods received, and laid before the Directors every meeting.

10. A minute book to be kept of all board orders as well as of any incident occurring in the station out of the ordinary, and of all the visitors.

11. Strict accounts to be kept. Coals to be accepted on receipt. To be credited daily as charged into the retorts. Coal account to be debited with what is drawn from the retort and credited with what is used in Furnace and

what is sold. Meters to be debited with what is received and credited with what is sold or rented. Tubing and pipes to be debited with what is received and credited with what is sold. Meters to be debited with what is received and credited with what is sold or rented. Tubing and pipes to be debited with what is received and credited with what is sold or used.[101]

The last four rulings obviously applied to the secretary rather than the manager, who was relatively free to do as he pleased at certain stages in the day. This was not the case elsewhere. In 1855, Strabane Corporation virtually imprisoned the manager, demanding that he not leave the works 'from the time he came in in the morning till he goes home at night'![102] There may have been good reason for such extraordinary rulings. In 1872, for instance, the manager at Donaghadee was reprimanded for leaving the works in the charge of a labourer who allowed the gasometer to rise too high. Little more than three weeks later, his resignation (with the customary months's notice) was accepted upon condition that he abandon the bottle![103]

The governing body of the Dundalk Gas Company – founded on 25 July 1836 – obviously had developed a very refined view of their manager's duties. In 1856 they decreed that he was

> to have charge of the works and property belonging to the company, the superintendence of all persons and workmen employed in their service. To be accountable for the manufacturing of gas, the quantity consumed by meter and the preparation of returns from making and the quarterly accounts for collection. To reside in the works and not to absent himself there upon exception on business or with permission form the Committee management. The manager to see that none of the Company's property shall leave the works before or after the hours appointed for the clerk to be in attendance and that all fittings etc. be charged by the clerk upon leaving the works. The manager to report to the Committee any case of intemperence he observes in the company's servants. To attend at the works daily from half-past nine until five o'clock so as to keep an account of the time and wages of all persons employed and to pay the same . . . in cash. To enter the sale or hiring of all property to the company in a Book to be provided for that purpose, and to issue a ticket for same . . . No property of any kind to leave the works without a ticket from the clerk.[104]

Indeed, Dundalk Gas Company even advised one new manager, in 1856, to proceed upon arrival 'to a Hotel in the Town, enquire for Mr M.B. Patterson . . . and he will instruct you how to act as it might be prudent for you to visit the works accompanied by the Directors who will point out your duties'.[105] The directors would not allow the men an opportunity to hoodwink or fraternise with their new manager on his first day! Other governing bodies did not possess such foresight, as suggested by 'the donkey affair' in Clonmel.

The 'donkey affair' began on 6 December 1901 when Alderman O'Connor asked who owned the donkey used for delivering coke at 1d. per hundredweight; he was informed by the secretary that the manager owned the donkey and pocketed the resultant profits.[106] On 10 December, the corporation minutes record that: 'Consequent upon a discussion relating to the delivery of coke it was proposed by the Chairman and unanimously resolved that the present arrangement for delivery of coke be discontinued at the end of the current month and that after that date coke be delivered free within the Borough'.[107] Only a month later did the responsible and magnanimous parties realise that no coke was being delivered at all, as they had failed to make an alternative arrangement. Clearly, the corporation had expected Mr Kneeshaw, Clonmel manager, to supply coke at his own expense. They eventually ordered that 'a Corporation horse and cart be sent to the Gas Works daily at 11 and 3 o'clock to deliver coke within the Borough pending other arrangements for this delivery'.[108] By the end of January they had changed their minds about the merits of free coke, stating that 'it was of little advantage to the poor' and was 'taken advantage of largely by parties who could well afford to pay for delivery'.[109] On 13 February 1902, it was decided to abandon the idea of supplying coke at the corporation's expense and revert to the old scheme — but with the purchase of the manager's donkey and cart.[110] The corporation had taken a rather circuitous route to arrive at profit!

COMPANY-CONSUMER RELATIONS

There was general suspicion on the part of the public that managers profited by deceiving customers and citizens. There is little doubt, for example, that managers had difficulty in convincing people of the merits, safeguards or the technicalities of gas measurement and meters. In the minutes of the Armagh Gaslight Company of July 1848, for instance, it was 'resolved that it be explained to [a customer] that while it is possible for the gas to pass through the meter without having registered, it is quite impossible for the meter to register without the gas passing through it . . . and that therefore the charge is correct'.[111] Indeed, in the legal wrangle between the Carlow Gas Company and Patrick Molloy, baker, in April 1862, the manager, swore that 'all meters are so constructed that they cannot go wrong'.[112] However, not everyone took this line in court. The case of John Delea against the United General Gas Company was heard before Justice O'Brien in Cork in July 1858. John Connors, a former employee of the United General who now worked for the Cork Gas Consumers' Company, admitted to the court that 'it sometimes happened that the meter did not indicate the true quantity of gas consumed; it might indicate a greater or less quantity'.[113] Meters could be poorly fitted, subject to environmental conditions like fire and frost,[114] or simply tampered with, as suggested by the following instances in Cork between 1860 and 1882.

Tilting Meters and Hatpins

In November 1860, Denny Lane stated that 'the shop of Mr Wynne [baker] . . . was visited by Mr Mahony [Director], Mr Still and himself and they had found the meter tilted forward' as reported previously.[115] Upon the removal, testing and tilting of the said meter, it was discovered that 'it allowed a larger percentage of gas to pass without registration and that at a certain point a steady flame was given although the meter ceased to register any quantity'.[116] In January 1862, 'a report was made by Mr Still relative to the fraudulent use of gas by W.J. Hegarty who had removed the meter and connected the inlet to the outlet pipe by flexible tubing'.[117] In December 1871, it was reported that a meter was positioned in such a way as to prevent the closing of a door 'by Lynch of Cornmarket Street', and that a meter had been fitted 'back to front' (service to the outlet and fittings to the inlet pipe to prevent registration) at Mr Murphy's premises in Shandon Street.[118] In January 1872, attention was drawn to the existence of 'some persons purporting to be employed by the company' who had entered houses on the pretext of examining meters and had effected a robbery in one case.[119] In July 1881, it was decided not to charge a poor shopkeeper for a meter destroyed by fire.[120]

These occurrences were not peculiar to Cork alone. In Dungannon in April 1888, the manager reported that he had found Mr P.J. Devlin's meter tilted on two separate occasions so that gas would pass through it without being registered against the consumer.[121] R. McElborough, a meter fitter in Belfast, recalled one instance when 'on top of the index box we found a tiny hole where a point of a hat pin . . . could be inserted between the index wheels' in such a way as to prevent the wheels from moving and registering consumption of gas.[122]

In Armagh, in December 1903, 'the Directors could not see their way to supply, free of cost, a new meter to take the place of one destroyed by fire at W.D. Slewant & Co.[123] In April 1899, the manager at Larne 'reported that in taking the indications of the meters for the March quarter, he found that T.F. English of Mill Street had, in making alterations to his shop removed the Company's meter and connected his gas supply with the Company's mains without the Company's consent'.[124] On being informed that he was liable for a sum of £9 or more, the culprit stated that 'he was sorry and that he had not done so with any fraudulent intent but through ignorance', and undertook not to do so again.[125] The directors considered publishing the apology from the culprit in the local newspaper as warning to others but decided not to do so as it might reflect upon Mr English's character.[126] Instead, they issued a strong warning to the responsible builder, James Finis.

Admittedly, these instances of company-consumer relations were abnormal, with most customers simply paying their bills and treating their meters with respect. Customers naturally distrusted meters which registered 'an unaccountable increase in consumption from that of previous terms'. In the early days, before the companies supplied free meters, consumers resented having to purchase or rent a device designed to help deprive them of money. For their part, managers were reasonably content with meters which allowed them the opportunity to abandon the old untrustworthy system of contracted hours of consumer consumption and the consequent checking to preclude robbery.[127] In 1831, for instance, James Carfran, manager of the Londonderry Gaslight Company, obviously delighted in this dictate.

> The Company have determined upon supplying all places where the consumption of gas is known to be uncertain only by meter; and they will likewise insist on meters being used when frauds are committed upon them.[128]

Managers did experience some difficulties with meters, however. In 1866 in Ennis, for instance, there was an interesting case of a grocer's dry-meter registering less then the company's wet-meter.[129] In Naas, the public meters performed in a very curious fashion, so that in 1874, a Mr Daniel was forced to argue his case against the Town Commissioners.[130] Indeed, Downpatrick's Charles Mearns used to get very excited and annoyed when 'he got orders from the directors to falsify the meters or commit any other fraud'![131] Most disputes related to meters were anticipated, however, with the company taking the average of previous terms as the sum owed by reluctant debtors. In Ballymoney, the company decreed that 'As an interruption to the action of the meter may occur from various causes, the Company . . . have the right of charging the customers with the same quantity of gas as may have been used by them at the same period of the previous year, in proportion to the number of burners'. They stated that this rule was to be adopted 'in all and every case of disputed accuracy that may occur in regard to the meter'.[132] Indeed, with the introduction of the slot meter such difficulties were further reduced, although managers were not always quick to adopt them. In Dungannon, a number of pre-payment meters were found to be unsatisfactory to the gas company in April 1896 because they all allowed more than the 14 cubic feet of gas equivalent to 1d. The manager took another six months to satisfy himself of the advantages of these new slot meters and order fifty. Neither were the new meters always appreciated by the customers. In Newtownards, one customer complained that

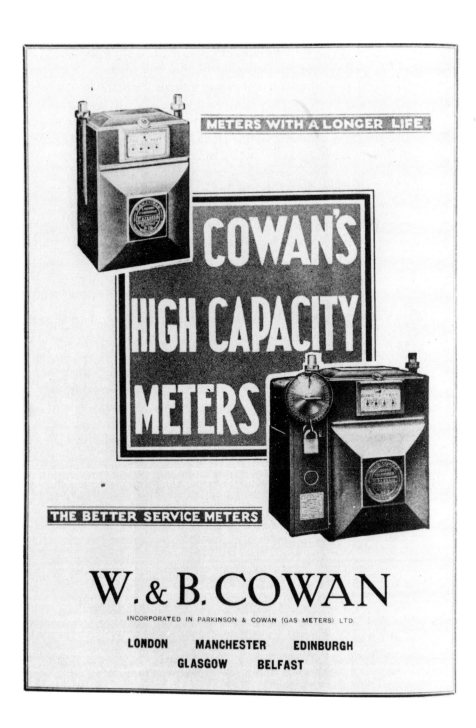

trying to satisfy meters with pennies was like trying to fill an elephant with a biscuit! He may not have been far from the mark. In May 1938, a shortage of copper coins in Belfast was attributed to their imprisonment in the city's 62,000 prepayment meters. Apparently, the daily collection amounted to £1,000 – but collectors had been otherwise engaged for a week! There was, of course, a danger that the collector could be robbed as a result of slot meters. In Cork it was suggested that the younger generation's popular sport of breaking the gas lamps was better than the pilfering of a day's takings.[133] In Carlow, the collector was accompanied by either the manager or his deputy 'to carry the heavy load of coins to the Bank'.[134]

Works Problems

Even in Carlow, managers had better things to be doing than making friendly financial visitations or making costly court appearances! When the second gas company was founded there in 1846, an unexpected difficulty was encountered in the construction of the tank for the gasholders. As soon as it was erected, the huge cistern was found to leak considerably. Since it was built on a powerful spring, the situation did not improve when the cistern's interior walls and floor were thickly coated with cement. An attempt to crush down the spring with the help of a floor made of large stone blocks proved ineffective, as did the brain-power of the renowned railway engineer William Dargan. Indeed, the situation was only remedied, after considerable effort and expense, with the suggestion that the spring be redirected by means of a conduit constructed below the tank. Needless to say, all such challenges to managerial ingenuity did not evaporate with the successful construction of a water-tight tank for the containment of gas. The gasworks at Carlow was situated on the left bank of the River Barrow to help facilitate the supply of coal, and was accordingly subject to occasional flooding. As a result, side or outside producers had to be devised, adopted and constructed.[135]

Carlow Gas Works was not the only one to suffer such seasonal setbacks and unforeseen problems. In Newtownards, in 1911, for instance, the house containing the governors which regulated the supply of gas through the mains was shattered by a gas explosion. This might have had great ramifications had not the manager, W.H. Roberts, promptly turned off the gas at the mains.[136] In Clonmel, on 25 April 1871, the newly repaired gasholder simply tilted over.[137] Some years earlier in March 1864, there was a major explosion in the purification plant of the Dublin Alliance Gas Company. It blew the roof off a purifying tank into an adjoining lane, smashed neighbouring windows, scattered insecure slates, shook nearby foundations, roused sleeping citizens and 'caused no small amount of consternation' without injuring departing employees.[138] In Lisburn in

February 1957, a gust of wind stole 70,000 cubic feet of gas from a gasholder (it had done so on two previous occasions since 1917). In November 1959, gales in Coleraine tore a 10-ton metal chimney from its base shortly before thirty men arrived for work in the building.

As suggested by the following entries relating to Dan Lawlor's life at the Dublin Alliance Gas Works between 1849 and 1854, managerial responsibilities could be quite frustrating, even with a salary of £120 per annum by way of compensation.[139] In March 1849, the columns of the new holder fell, causing serious damage to the tank; fears were expressed that the old gasholder might not withstand the storms. The board considered having a wall built to shield the holders from the wind, but Dan Lawlor entertained doubts about this, having seen the old one, only eight feet high, being blown down in 1839. In July 1849, it was observed that the tar scrubbers were causing further harm, while it was clear by August that the holders' new rollers were 'a perfect failure'. On 28 September, while emptying the tank of water, the contractors' foreman forgot to remove the manhole cover causing the holder to collapse – to the consternation of Dan Lawlor who 'did not expect to have repairs made until December'.

In January 1850, the frost was so heavy in Dublin that fires had to be lit around the holder tank. By March, another holder had been successfully erected, only to show up the inadequacy of the exhauster, and it burst in June 1850. In October 1850, concern was expressed about meeting the city's growing heating requirements for the winter, while relevant parties recognised that they were swamped with a stock of tar. In May 1851, a tar tank capable of holding 25,000 gallons was erected. But by July, with the production of 300 gallons of tar per day, it was thought that a ship would be necessary to take it away! It was also feared in July that the holder, which was found to be as much as six inches out of perpendicular in May, would not be finished by the winter. By March 1852, the new gasholder was working well. But in September, there was an explosion in the purifier house which blew off the roof and released the gas. Life was certainly eventful, even for an engineer like Lawlor, who could still find time to investigate the merits of water-gas, iron oxide purification and ammonia scrubbers, while extending his knowledge to Mullingar, Cavan and Trim.[140]

INTEMPERENCE

Dan Lawlor was obviously appreciated as his salary was raised from £120 to £500 in five years.[141] Indeed, his managerial abilities were not confined simply to the technological dimension, as he showed considerable insight by suggesting that poor attendance among retort workers through drunkenness might be curbed with the employment of eight to ten new stokers.

Intemperance was understandably frequent in such a demanding environment; the problem was how to deal with it. In Dundalk, in November 1891, the manager G.R. Love reported that 'drinking during working hours, leaving the works without permission, and tending to do the least amount of work possible have been the characteristics of the men and . . . I have at times been placed in pretty strange corners'.[142] Love concluded with these remarks: 'Perhaps the men are not altogether to blame as they were certainly managed in these ways by the later manager . . . I am prepared to deal leniently with them to save further trouble'.[143] Interestingly enough, 'the late manager' Mr Featherstone, had only reported injuries suffered by the men at the works in order to secure compensation for them![144]

Approaches to the problem of on-the-job drinking obviously varied, with a certain degree of tolerance being extended in some instances. The treatment of Alfred Laffan in Wexford was one such case.[145] In January 1872, a special meeting of the directors was called both to admonish this clerk and collector for intemperance and neglect of duty and to warn him that a similar complaint in future would lead to his dismissal. In February 1873, it was resolved unanimously that Anthony Laffan be called upon to resign his position. In March, it was agreed not to accept his resignation upon his assurances and a bond of £200. By May, the manager Mr Lyne was authorised to dismiss Laffan should he again fail to perform his duties. In November the directors allowed Laffan to tender his resignation, before rejecting his application for the job a week later.

In Cork, the reaction to incompetence through alcoholic beverage was more instantaneous, with frequent suspensions or dismissals. Here too, however, the general approach was tempered with a certain degree of mercy and sound sense. This attitude was underlined by an incident in September 1884. After reading a testimonial from James Walsh, who had been discharged for leaving an escape of gas after changing a meter, the directors ordered 'that he may be employed at the works but, until he takes the total abstinence pledge, he is not to be put back into meter changing'.[146] In October 1895, the Cork directors gave further evidence of this positive prejudice by giving free gas for the illumination of the Father Mathew Statue in Patrick Street![147]

WORKERS' WAGES AND CONDITIONS

Although no laughing matter to those in authority, drunkenness could serve as a humorous diversion, lightening or dissipating complaints about the quality of gas produced, especially at Christmas.[148] However, it could also be used as an excuse for not increasing workers' wages. In Coleraine, in

April 1905, Mr Gribbon earnestly opposed Mr McDonald's generous motion for an increase in stokers' pay; it was Gribbon's view that, at three shillings a day, the stokers were fairly dealt with 'and some of them do not always spend their wages for the benefit of their families'.[149] Apparently, Mr Gribbon was a firm believer in public economy and a strong promoter of family consumption! Mr McDonald had argued on this occasion that

> the men were working for very low wages and their job was a most laborious one, and one at which they lose a great deal of sweat. Their wages only come to 3½d. per hour and they worked seven days in the week, and twelve hours for a shift each day . . . and . . . had no assistance during the summer months – all the winter help being dismissed. . . . The stokers had to bring the coal in from the store, to weigh it, to charge the retorts and to draw them, and to cool the coke. Considering that this application only meant an increase of £3 18s. 0d. per annum or in other words that the men's wages should be made 25s. 0d. a week the year round, he thought the Committee should have granted the request [by the two stokers].[150]

Indeed, when it was pointed out to him that the present rate was comparatively high for labourers, that only one retort operated in the summer as opposed to six in the winter, and that the men were doing practically nothing for six hours out of the twelve hour shift, McDonald further contended that

> these men are not ordinary labourers. It is not every man that could be brought in, from the quay or off the streets, to do work of this kind. It is practically skilled labour and a man has to be several years in the gasworks before he can do the work properly which is extracting all the gas out of the coal that can be got . . . more gas was required in the Summer season for gas engines because water was scarcer at that time and not available for power. The individual who worked twelve hours a day in the heat of the summer and in the heat of the gasworks was better entitled to full wages and he had to work twelve hours on the Sabbath as well.[151]

Nevertheless, McDonald's view was opposed by nine votes to three.

By 1911, however, the situation in Coleraine had changed a little in favour of the retort men. By this time, the manager, Mr J. Taylor, kept two stokers at work per shift from August to May, with shifts lasting twelve hours and beginning at either 8 a.m. or 8 p.m. Foremen stokers and chargers were paid 25s. 0d. per week, with one week's paid holiday in the year. Second men or drawers were paid 20s. 0d. from August to September, 26s. 0d. from October to November, 23s. 6d. from December to January, 22s. 6d. from February to April and 21s. 0d. from April to August. Foremen stokers were even relieved from duty every Sunday, without deductions, during the months of May, June and July and replaced by second men who received 3s. 0d. for Sunday duty.[152] Indeed, conditions elsewhere were not as good at the time. In Clonmel, in 1911, for instance, the stokers asked for an increase in wages and outlined their working conditions as follows:

> We the undersigned stokers hereby make application for an increase of pay to 25s. 0d. per week, standing wages all the year round. At present, we are employed 365 days in each year and in future we want every second Sunday off . . . as it is most unreasonable to expect any men to remain constantly on their feet for quite 22 hours.[153]

Mr R. Kneeshaw, manager of the Clonmel works, elaborated in greater detail to the Gas Committee of the corporation.[154] Evidently, six men were employed during the summer months to keep three beds (eighteen retorts) in operation, while eight men were employed during the remaining eight months to feed seven beds. Day duty lasted a cycle of six drawings and chargings at two hourly intervals from 6 a.m. The men worked day and night duty alternately, and were paid an average 3s. 2d. per day from May to September and about 3s. 5d. from October to March.

Conditions in 1911 varied from place to place. In Drogheda, Mr H.W. Saville employed three stokers for about five months in summer at 26 shillings per fifty-six hour week, with shifts arranged so that every man would have one day off in every three weeks.[155] For three months of the year, four men were employed on twelve-hour shifts, with two earning 26s. per week and the others 23s. 0d. There were four days' holidays for each of the four regulars but no extra pay for Sunday work or alternative hours on that day, with two extra wheelers being taken on at 20s. 0d. per week during November.[164] In Ballymena, William Nisbet had two stokers on each twelve-hour shift; two leading stokers earned 25s. 0d. per week and the others 20s. 0d. The men were given three days' holiday with pay during June and were helped by a barrowman on each shift from October to March.

In Tralee, J.E. Enright employed four stokers all year round. The first he paid 25s. 0d. per week and the rest received 23s. 6d. Shifts were from 7 a.m. to 6 p.m. with one hour allowed for breakfast and dinner altogether. During the summer, no work was undertaken on Sundays between 6 a.m. and 6 p.m., although work besides stoking could be expected during the rest of the week. During winter, the men were paid extra for Sunday labour.[156]

In Bangor, Barker Mitchell ran shifts of eight hours' duration. He paid 28s. 6d. per week, with three days' holidays per man and double time for work undertaken on Christmas Day and Easter Monday.[157] By today's standards, the gas industry was extremely demanding in terms of the hours worked, labour expended and pay awarded. Indeed, relative rates of pay may be judged by the fact that, in Clonmel at this time, a lamplighter's overcoat cost 20 shillings and his boots 12, even if supplied free by management![158]

Stokers in Dublin wore clogs — and with good reason. R.McElborough recalled that he had seen stokers in gasworks standing on hot platforms, their feet almost blistered as they discharged the retorts. Labour conditions in Belfast were amply outlined by McElborough who served under three managers – Messrs Stelfox, Sharp and Smith – and ran into some difficulties as a result of union activities. McElborough began at the bottom as one of the four boys who attended either the meter fillings or lamplighters and who could be seen pushing carts at a time when the gas consumers in Belfast were either middle or higher class citizens, and when the gas department was 'an easy going affair.'[159] McElborough's foreman as a boy was an unpopular socialist named W. Gordon who was trained as a sheet-metal worker and who taught a class in the technical school after finishing his work in the gas department. Even without Gordon's influence, McElborough resented being paid a shilling less than his due. Realising that the other boys were more interested in promotion than social justice, McElborough resigned after little more than three years to become a tram conductor. He returned as a meter fitter at a time when slot meters were being introduced. The gas department had been transformed into a hive of activity, with the resultant applications from thousands of working-class jobseekers. McElborough seriously considered his prospects of promotion at a time when craftsmen earned 36s. 0d. a week, labourers 18s.6d. and boys 10s. 6d. Inspectors earned £104 a year and the subordinate complaints officials were entitled to a pension. McElborough set his sights on reaching the complaints department but soon found that progress there was slow and promotion corrupt. It was, he wrote 'a matter not about brains or qualifications'.[160] Apparently, by the outbreak of the First World War, 'the promotion business' had become somewhat of a scandal and an examination was introduced to rubber stamp or legitimise the process. Being poor at fractions and abstract reasoning, McElborough believed that the examination was more suitable for the civil service than the gas industry, noting that candidates like himself lost a day's earnings for attempting to improve their stations. In any case, he did not succeed in convincing his examiners of his competency to deal with customers' complaints.

McELBOROUGH AND LABOUR RELATIONS

There was only one alternative path for an ambitious man like McElborough, and so he became involved in the labour movement.

It was heart breaking to think that we were unable to seek an increase or better our conditions. If we got Easter Monday as a holiday we had to then work on Easter Sunday at 6, otherwise we lost Monday pay even if you come in at breakfast time. The rule applied to the 12th July and Xmas and every holiday . . . it required a strike in the Gas works before we made any progress.

The strike in question lasted for two weeks and was not helped (from the strikers' point of view) by the fact that some of the lamplighting staff volunteered to work in the gasworks. Apparently, the gas committee gave the manager a free hand and unlimited funds. In turn, the manager supplied the strike-breakers with boiler suits, a canteen and beds so that they could comfortably ignore their fellow workmates from behind closed doors. Nevertheless, some ventured forth. One strike-breaker left for home and family by the back gate; he was caught and would have been thrown into the river but for the regrettable fact that he had a club foot! After pleading that he had a large family and promising to stop working, the man was released, only to secure a police escort in coming to and from the works and earning a promotion for his opposition to the demands of labour. Others were not so fortunate, and McElborough obviously appreciated the fact that one of the strike-breakers was discovered, before the police knew, and received 'a severe mauling' which ruffled his new boiler suit.

With financial support from London, however, the strikers succeeded in securing written agreements from their employers. As a result, the labour movement was injected with a certain vitality. Even so, progress was slow as suggested by the career of one activist, T. Boyd, who had commenced work on the clerical staff only to be transferred to meter testing. According to McElborough, 'the test-shop was about the worst place he could have been placed in as you inhaled gas from when you entered until you left and you were always in a sort of stupor which inclined sleep'. In any case, Boyd was compelled through ill health to leave within two years of the appointment.

McElborough himself was earmarked as a trouble-maker by the management and singled out for special treatment, or so he would have us believe from his memoirs. During the First World War, the boys attending the lamplighters and meter fitters decided that their wages were of little use. They refused to go out with their carts, and eventually divided upon the question of continuing their insolence at the cost of possible promotion. McElborough, their adviser, was 'looked upon as the one who had caused the trouble'. McElborough joined the war effort to avoid suffering any further isolation. Little did he know that his future with the gas company was secure. With the troubles in 1922, the military insisted on the streets being lit even though the locals preferred the darkness which would allow them to escape snipers' bullets. When the boy responsible for tending the lamps refused to enter Seaforde Street and Slate Street McElborough was given the job and threatened with dismissal if he refused.

Exhausters in use at Belfast Gasworks in the early 1920s. These were compressors used for drawing gas from the gas-making plant.

Condensers for cooling gas at Belfast in the early 1920s. This involved, among other processes, the condensing of tar and water from rain-gas.

I had a wife and family and was threatened with dismissal if I refused to do this work. I would have given it up. I can't tell how I got the cart into this area. I ran miles with it and got safely into Mervue Street and into Seaforde Street with rifles cracking overhead. When I arrived with the lamps and fittings, I was surrounded by a number of men and women who told me to clear out. I had to express my predicament as a workman. It was the women who carried the day in my favour. I was told that every lamp and fitting that I fitted up would be smashed when the lights were on. . . . The people in the area never interfered with me, but there was a time when I had to clear out when someone who lived in the district had been shot by a sniper. It was the snipers on the roof and back windows who were the danger. Anyone seen within the range of their gun was their target and they found out later through the press what side he belonged to. . . . My only dread was when I was standing on the ladder putting up a lamp. Bullets that I supposed meant for me went through the lamp reflectors.

At the time, to the bewilderment of some inhabitants who wished to turn them off, some lamps did not need an attendant as they were controlled by the pressure from the gasworks with the help of a weights mechanism and 'a lit by-pass'. It was McElborough's bad fortune that all lamps were not thus equipped. In any case, he survived the traditional lamps and occasional violence to rescue meters from burning houses on the Falls Road before they were blown up with the spate of house burnings which followed the incidental sniper fire! Only with the Blitz of the Second World War did McElborough collapse while removing meters from burning buildings. After receiving 5s. 9d. for each of the seven weeks of his sick leave from the gas department, he returned to work, retiring after a serious case of gas poisoning at the age of fifty-nine with a pension of £1 a week. Naturally, he complained to the gas manager that this pension was not much after so many years' service. However, as he ruefully remarked, the managers's hands were tied by the gas committee, which consisted of a butcher, baker and candle-stick maker who wouldn't have known a gasholder from a vertical retort!

CAPITAL AND LABOUR

Although McElborough's experiences may be dismissed as exceptional, there is no denying that the scales of company justice fell favourably on the side of management who naturally did not welcome improved working conditions for the men at the expense of shareholder expectations. Undoubtedly, it was a profitable business, for some more than others. In 1886, the Parsonstown Gas Company declared a dividend of 5 percent although there was decline in gas consumption in the town because of the depressed state of business.[161] Similarly, the gas company in Carrickfergus declared a modest dividend of 5½ percent in 1887.[162] Indeed, with the declaration of an 8 percent dividend at the 19th Annual Meeting of the Skibbereen Gas Light & Coke Company in 1887, the good Father O'Leary . warmly appreciated the fact that 'not every business can declare such a dividend these days!'[163] At the time, the Kinsale Gas Company could only manage a 3 percent dividend.[164] As suggested by a call for a 6 percent dividend instead of one at 4½ percent, Kilkenny shareholders in 1895 appreciated fat profits which, by the very nature of the early manufacturing industry, were largely governed by the costs of coal and labour.[165] In Newry in 1898, the cost of carting and storing coal was nearly £3,000; the workmen's wages came to just over £800 while the combined salaries of the manager, collector and secretary amounted to nearly £400. Thus expenditure of some £4,000 amounted to nearly two-thirds of the bill for the manufacture and sale of gas.[166]

Unlike the sometimes fluctuating prices of gas, coal, coke, tar and the like, the demands of labour were largely independent of the dictates of the market place, and could be controlled and manipulated to company advantage. Labour relations were no fun, as suggested by this instance in Cork in September 1872. After Mr Still had directed inspector O'Connor to comply with the demands of Messrs Walsh, Connolly, Hegarthy and Cullnane, the inspector returned and told Still that he was afraid to do any of the men's business through threats of being beaten. O'Connor was dismissed when he could not state who threatened him![167] Violence and rough justice went hand in hand in such a demanding environment. In Cashel in 1881, during a squabble about the arrangement of pressure, Mr Pyne, after eighteen years in the gasworks assaulted the man in charge and left the works after 'telling Corcoran to make gas as he liked'.[168]

Lamplighters

Within the wage earning sector, there was also a hierarchy as reflected in Dungannon in 1987. The company saw fit to raise the wages of the two firemen from 16s. 0d. to 17s. 0d. They continued paying the yard-man 15s. 0d. a week and increased the lamplighters' wage of 14s. 0d. by a shilling while engaging the services of an assistant yard-man during the winter months at 12s. 0d. a week.[169] Lamplighters were obviously considered the least significant. In 1899, lamplighters in Enniskillen were paid 6s. 0d. per week, 16s. 0d. in Clonmel and Newry, about 17s. 6d. in Galway and Lisburn and 20s. 0d. in Waterford.[170] Conditions varied along with pay; the two Enniskillen lamplighters tended 117 lamps, four men tended 187 lamps in Clonmel, three tended 271 in Newry, two were needed for Galway's 163 lamps, three in Lisburn for 186, and six in Waterford for 400.[171] As testified by the initial failure of Cork Corporation workmen to light and quench lamps effectively in February 1871,[172] there was more to

A delivery of coal to Clonmel Gasworks, circa 1840s.

the job than first met the eye. To begin with, lamplighters had to carry a ladder in order to mount, attend and descend – some three or four hundred times an evening.[173] Before improved technology advanced their lot, they had to overcome adverse road and weather conditions. An interesting insight into such work was provided in 1884 by the lamplighters of Dublin, when they asked for a raise of sixpence because

> during the past year there has been a great deal of extra duty imposed on us, such as having to get out of bed any hour during the night when the police would call us for the purpose of relighting lamps which would be put out by rain or wind or otherwise extinguished by some malicious person. We also have to supply ourselves with the necessary requirements for our work, such as chamois oil and matches, which amount to a considerable sum at the end of the year.[174]

At the time, Dublin had 3,750 lamps and only twenty-five lamplighters.[175] Dublin was not the only place where lamplighters were expected to supply their own 'equipment', as the minutes of the Armagh Gaslight Company record an increase in lamplighters' wages by a shilling 'owing to the high prices of provisions'.[176]

Indeed, lamplighters were expected to do more than simply light and extinguish lamps in some cases. In Clonmel, Mr Kneeshaw admitted that 'only one man gives his whole time to the lamps, the others are engaged for the most part on other work', while answering the Gas Committee's contention that the works was overstaffed.[177] Apparently, one 'lamplighter' weighed the coke, another attended the fitter and a third kept the coke yard. Nor was this unusual: in Newcastle in 1911, one lamplighter called Moore was also baths caretaker (with the help of his wife) and had to rise at 5 a.m. on some occasions.[178] In Coleraine, the opinion was expressed in 1905 that 'the lamplighters were doing work that was not easy' as they worked all day for the Council before lighting all the lamps of the town.[179] Opinions naturally varied on the delicate question of remuneration. Mr Kennedy argued that 'any man who had to go out two or three times a day to light and extinguish lamps should have better wages [than the then average 19s. 0d. per week], and if an extra 2s. 6d. per week would make him do his work better, he thought that there should be no objection'.[180] Indeed, Mr Glenn, to the obvious amusement of all present, noted that lamplighters could detect crime, while Mr Henry observed that they had to do twice as much work now as the year before. However, Mr McFetter said that the gas manager thought that the lamplighters were paid well enough; the chairman reminded everyone that no lamps had to be lit between mid-May and the end of August before the motion was defeated by a single vote.

Company lamplighters were in especially vulnerable positions as they could easily lose their jobs when cosmetic economies were made to reduce the company's bill for public lighting. In April 1871, following the corporations's decision to tend the public lamps in Cork, two redundant lamplighters wrote to Denny Lane, saying they were unable to secure gainful employment having spent twenty and ten years respectively at a job which extended little qualification or experience for doing anything else.[181] Similarily, in Lisburn in 1909, with the corporation's impending acquisition of the gas works, readers of *The Lisburn Herald* discovered that the company intended to discharge the lamplighters during the summer months in the interest of company profits, in spite of the fact that the men in question had served the company for twenty years and did necessary repair and preparatory work when free from lamplighting duties.[182] Anyone could do the job, as suggested by the fact that boys carrying light ladders and 6-feet lengths of half-inch pipe could tend the fifty lamps in Ballina.[183] Indeed, the process of lighting and quenching became so simplified that *The Lisburn Herald* could report in 1905 that a wren had managed to operate the relevant chains in the gas lamp in which she had reared her brood![184]

Life with the Navan Corporation was no more secure, with lamplighters having to endure or manipulate the occasional politics of re-election.[185] In Dungannon, a lamplighter was only re-appointed in 1899 on condition that 'he report himself' to a member of the Lighting Committee during calendar moonlit nights so that he could receive instructions about 'whether or not to light up in case of unexpected darkness'.[186] Admittingly, most lamplighters were probably too preoccupied with the prospect of sleep or the drudgery of foul weather and its attendant dangers to worry about the question of security of employment. In 1886, *The Londonderry Standard* brought its readers' attention to the plight of John Manley from Bridgewater who had spent twenty-nine years tending lamps and who had suffered from severe rheumatism after the first seventeen years of dedicated service.[187]

WORKING WITH GAS

Apparently, lamplighters were not the only gasmen to operate the lamps at unsociable hours in the interests of public relations. In Ennis in 1890, the manager W.J. Wynne declared that he had endeavoured to give every satisfaction, both to the commissioners and the lamplighters, setting out at midnight and 5 a.m. to repair public lamps in order 'to make matters comfortable' between them.[188] Nor were lamplighters the only ones to fall from ladders in the interests of gas supply. In October 1896, Mr Kneeshaw reported that 'Mr Mackessey, the gas fitter, had met with an accident through the breaking of one of the sides of the step ladder on which he was engaged at fitting work outside the brewery and that he had not been able to attend his duties'.[189] Little more than four years before, a gas fitter had fallen to his death from the Clock Tower in Youghal.[190]

There was also the danger of explosions, as suggested by the case of Charles Toner, a gasworks employee in Limavady in 1907 who brought down the ceiling upon himself while looking, with a lighted match, for an escape of gas in Andrew F. Cray's premises in Market Street.[191] However, more frequent among gas fitters were incidents of gas poisonings. In his memoirs, R. McElborough recalls that he once thought that gas fitters were always drunk but that he knew better after forty-one years' experience, having 'lost count of the number of times I came out . . . like a drunken man and the times I lay unconscious for fifteen minutes before I came round'.[192] In Belfast, McElborough observed that fitters were often gassed in confined spaces under counters and cupboards in which a light could not be taken; fitters had to grope in the dark for fittings and meter while leaving air out of the gas pipe before attaching it by touch to the meter.[193] He remembered that his first meter-fitting job was in a provisions shop in Cromac Street.

> I had to change a 5 ft fitting, the meter was like thousands of other meters in shops, it was below the window next to the stairs and there was a large marble slab above it. I had to crouch underneath the slab on my stomach and disconnect and catch the fitting, you had to work in the dark and after I had disconnected it, I had to fit on a new one. I always carried a cork for when I felt the gas overcoming me I put the cork in the service until the boy pulled me out until I recovered from the effects of the gas in my system. At the second attempt, I succeeded in getting the thread of the cock on the service. I remembered nothing more until I recovered to see my own boy and the shop boy and the inspector. I always told my boy when I kicked with my foot to pull me out.

The effects of such gas poisoning varied from pain and giddiness of the head, nausea, vomiting, confusion of intellect and general prostration of strength to death.[194] Fitters and service-layers lost all energy through frequent exposure,[195] and only hospital or funeral cases were recorded in company minutes.

Certainly, there was a sound reason for placing wet-meters in such awkward spots at the expense of gas fitters. In passing through the wet-meter, the gas absorbed some of the water in terms of vapour, hence the need to top up the water in the meter every three months.[196] When this vapour was in turn exposed to currents of cold air, it naturally condensed into water and could exert additional pressure on the gas to produce 'intermitting light'.[197] Apparently, part of the art of gas fitting was to maintain a fall or inclination of all service pipes towards the meter which, accordingly, had to be placed at the lowest point of the service.[198] The danger from exposure, however, was related to the type of gas being produced by the company. Ordinary coal-gas contained in average about 6 percent carbon monoxide while water-gas contained no less than 30 percent

125

to 40 percent of carbon monoxide.[199] The chances of recovering from exposure to ordinary coal-gas were seven times greater than if exposed to water-gas, which had little advantage to the consumer except its relative cheapness.[200] Indeed, its cost was noted in the *Belfast Evening Telegraph*, in November 1893, with a brief description of how it was produced.

> It is difficult to convey the technical details of the process but it may be stated that it consists in its first stage in the breaking up of water in contact with incandescent coke thereby producing a generous mixture of hydrogen and carbonic oxide. This gas is in itself non-luminous but it is rendered luminous by the spraying through it of paraffin distillate. A large stock of oil has been stored at the works and when the plant is finished the new gas will be immediately available. If oil continues at the present price it is likely that the new system will be very largely adopted as an excellent gas is produced at a somewhat cheaper rate than coal-gas of a high quality. . . . the process is an entirely new one in Ireland and has only been adopted by the London Gaslight and Coke Company. The Belfast instillation will be the most perfect one in the United Kingdom. The system is very largely adopted in America . . . the Belfast installation is the latest development.[201]

A professor of chemistry at Trinity College, and a professor of pathology at University College, Dublin, did not take such a positive view of Dublin's adoption of the French and American practices; at the turn of the century, they stressed that carburetted water-gas was extremely dangerous.[202] At the time, there were 1,614 gas works in the United Kingdom producing about 156,665,269,000 cubic feet of gas, of which 10 billion cubic feet was carburetted water-gas.[203]

Undoubtedly, the poisonous aspects of carburetted water-gas could prove useful. In June 1928, for instance, a number of men were engaged in laying a 12-inch main under the footpath of a suburban Belfast road bordered by a dense privet hedge in which a hive of wasps were resident.

> One of the men threw his coat over the hedge . . . [when] about a dozen wasps rushed out and asked him, in no uncertain language, what he meant by it. Without waiting to reply the man went down the road at the double, the wasps in hot pursuit, one of their number getting in a well planted sting in the back of the neck of the enemy. The coat was recovered by a *coup-de-main*, but whenever the men approached the neighbourhood of the nest . . . and struck the ground with pick or spade the wasps made angry demonstrations, and thus appeared to completely dominate the position. Headquarters were then telephoned for instructions, on which the Chief of Staff suggested that a gas attack should be organised. This was quickly done . . . the enemy vanquished, the position rushed, the nest torn from the hedge, pinned up in a paper bag, and carried in triumph to Headquarters . . . [for] close observation.[204]

The gasholder on Sir John Rogerson's Quay, a well-known Dublin landmark.

Indeed, the use of gas in the Dogs and Cats Home in Belfast, for the purpose of extermination, apparently proved to be 'painless, effective and economical'. Of course, all this was of little consequence to people who met similar accidental fates and of little consolation to their grieving families. In February 1895, John Donoghue, a Cork service layer who had tapped a four-inch main for a two-inch rider, without inserting bladders in the main as ordered, was overcome by an escape of gas while adjusting a bend in the tapped hole. He died before reaching the North Infirmary. His ordinary wage at the time would have been 24s. 0d., with overtime work bringing it 31s. 0d. a week to support five children and a wife who was with child.[205] Naturally, gas companies were in the business of making money; they did not hold themselves entirely responsible for employees who did not take proper safety precautions, or for occasional accidents and suicides. In Cork, as late as 1948, 'the Union claimed that recently certain workers had from time to time been suffering from gas poisoning', and it was pointed out that such workmen had disregarded the instructions to use gas masks which were specially provided for such contingency. In deserving cases, gas companies were willing to pay compensation.

LITIGATION

In other instances, they were sued. In May 1942, the Alliance and Dublin Consumers' Gas Company lost £300 with the discovery of 'Tobin's Oil Well'. In 1938, Patrick R.J. Tobin, his family and the customers who normally frequented his licensed establishment detected a smell of oil. They discovered that the vaults and cellar were flooded to a depth of several inches in 'beautiful thin golden oil which was welling up from the foundations of the house'; the gas company's pipeline from the quay was responsible. Men from the company then 'took possession of the cellar and pumped tremendous quantities of oil out of it', until November 1939, by which time Tobin had been forced to destroy large quantities of beverage and to contend with whining customers. Apparently, it had all begun as somewhat of a mystery to Mr Tobin, with business dropping off suddenly as dockers cycled off to another public house during their breaks in order to avoid the bad-breath cellars. The premises became known locally as 'Tobin's Oil Well'. The gas company probably did not want such an unlikely oil well being converted into a virtual gold mine at their expense, so they went to court to settle the issue as to whether or not the oil, which was conveyed through an underground pipe-line from the quayside, 'had been allowed' to escape and percolate into the premises of the publican residing at 82 Sir John Rogerson's Quay.

Other claims against gas undertakings lacked this humorous aspect, as they were related to injuries incurred through failure to resurface roads adequately, accidental poisonings and explosions, or labour relations problems. In 1901, the former Cavan manager, Patrick Maguire, claimed that the gas company owed him £40 5s. 2½d. after he had agreed to resign — and after he had taken the pledge. His salary had been £70 a year with a 5 percent commission on anything sold out of the yard, and on this last count he claimed £2. The remainder of his claim consisted of costs for repairs done to the company residence (as far back as 1882), or referred to the fact that he had always been paid £2 for each resetting of a retort and accordingly was entitled to £6 as he had employed a Mr McGuirke to reset ten of them for £4! Not surprisingly, Maguire was allowed only 21s. 6d. by the court.[206] Other instances were not so clear-cut. In 1920, Richard D. Perceval, Robert F. Fox and Captain Richard William Blackwood Ker opposed the Ballynahinch Gas Light Company for failure to pay £2 rent for each of the previous six years, as stipulated in a contract of May 1875. Apparently the company was not accustomed to paying rent, as a shareholder wrote in November 1913 that

> It was never the intention of the Landlord that any rent should be charged. The Ballynahinch Gas Company was organized in the year 1853, the promoters being Mr D.S. Ker, Mr W.P. Ancketell and several of the principal shopkeepers in the town. . . . The portion of ground on which the works were situated was then considered waste ground being close to the river and of no letting value. The Company was managed by the Estate Office, the Agent of the Estate up till 1880 being the Chairman and Treasurer of the Company and the Books of the Company etc. etc. were kept in the Estate Office and a clerk in the Office acted as the Secretary. In the year 1873 owing partly to mismanagement and largely to the then high price of coal, the company was worked at a loss and got into difficulties and in fact nearly for a year the works were closed. . . . Up till this time no rent had ever been paid. . . . With a view of realising the property some of the Directors thought they should secure a lease and sell out and Mr Marcus Gage who was then Chairman and Dr Dickson and Foreman made application for a lease of the property. However, while this negotiation was going on it became evident that great inconvenience would be experienced if the Gas Works were disposed of . . . and Mr Gage himself seeing this thought it better to continue the Gas Co. and he himself advanced £150, employed a new Manager, and carried on the Company until they tided over their difficulties. The application for a lease, or rather the perfecting of the lease, was then *abandoned* and as I believed no record of it was ever made in the Estate Books, nor was ever any rent sought for or paid from the date on which the Company started until this year.[207]

The Ballynahinch gas company lost the case, with little sympathy being extended to a company which was incorporated in 1856 with a capital of £1,095[208] and which was thought capable of paying rent like any other similar establishment.

GAS COMPANY PROSECUTIONS

The legal process was not entirely one-sided, with some gas companies prosecuting staff, citizens, customers, and urban councils on occasion. In 1926, the Downpatrick Gas Company claimed £350 from the urban council for 'steam-rolling, in the town, in such a way as to injure the gas mains';[209] such a development could not have been anticipated by the company's founding engineer Mr Colquhoun as far back as 1846. In 1945, W.J. Grey, secretary and general manager of the Alliance and Dublin Consumers' Gas Company, was charged with conspiring with a H.C. Hoskins to take nineteen electrical batteries, worth £117 and belonging to the company, and fraudulently doing so, upon the allegations of a dismissed employee.[210] More prevalent, and less complicated, were cases related to the breaking of lamps. In April 1871, the secretary of the gas company in Cork reported that a man named Goggin had broken fifteen lamps, and had been prosecuted, convicted and sentenced to two months' imprisonment 'to which would have been accompanied hard labour were it not for the state of his health'.[211] In 1885, *The Belfast and Newry Standard* delighted in warning 'nocturnal promenaders too frolicsomely inclined' that a London magistrate had seen fit to fine a gentleman £16 for breaking eight lamps, even though the culprit had been under the influence of drink.[212] Widely supported was the view held in 1927 by *The Ballina Herald*, that damage done to the street lamps was 'nothing short of wanton destruction and blackguardism . . . and only when the offenders are caught and an example made of them that such disgraceful conduct will be discontinued'.[213] Catching the offenders proved problematic and so the responses to the problem varied from place to place. In Cookstown in 1889, for instance, the constabulary were mobilised against lamp-abusers,[214] while in Kilkenny at about the same time, the 'puddling' of all the lamps from Patrick Street to the Convent was simply ignored.[215] In Enniskillen, in 1886, a reward of £10 was offered for the conviction of 'the perpetrators of the recent malicious breaking of the street lamps', or £5 promised to anyone with information leading to such arrests and convictions.[216] Yet not all cheeky or cheery offenders were prosecuted in accordance with public indignation or company practice. In December 1858, Denny Lane reported that 'a number of the Company's lamps had been broken by a party of military gentlemen and that he was about taking steps for the prosecution of the offenders when he had been waited upon by the adjutant of the regiment who had tendered the fullest apologies on their part, offering to pay for the damage and to contribute to charity any sum which the directors may fix'.[217] As a result, the North Infirmary gained £4, the South Infirmary £3 and the Mercy Hospital £3![218] In Cashel, a boy named Dillon escaped prosecution in 1880 even more lightly, by simply paying the gas company

The charming laneway at the back of the Dublin Gas Company premises.

for his 'breakages' and thereby getting the charges against him with-drawn.[219] Evidently, it was important that the offenders should not be poor!

In regard to the illegal tampering with gas meters, the legal process could be a double-edged sword; in making the offenders pay through the legal nose for their unwelcome ingenuity and initiative, the gas companies could not help publicising the fact and, by inference, promoting similar deceptions elsewhere. In January 1862, the directors of the Cork Gas Consumers' Company agreed that it would not be wise to have it generally known that W.J. Hegarthy had removed the meter and connected the relevant gaping pipes in order to deprive the company of its due deserts.[220] Clearly, the underlying motivation for this was that others might adopt the idea, although there was no such reluctance in making a public spectacle of Mr W. Collins, in 1872, by dragging him back from Geneva to make restitution for embezzling £1,000 while accountant in Cork.[221] The petty pilfering of coal by another less-gifted employee and the resultant period of imprisonment with hard labour was also widely publicised with the issuing of pamphlets by the company![222] In Cork, as elsewhere, deterrence was an important constituent of legal proceedings against offenders of company rights and practices. Indeed, the threat of legal action was directed against potential strikers, with eight strikers being prosecuted for breach of contract in 1901.[223] Interestingly enough, the magistrates in this case were unable to rule upon the issue, as required on a number of occasions, until the social sting had left the strike; even then they came down on the side of the men.

There is little doubt but that the profitable, private production of gas for public consumption was not always appreciated. In Wexford, in 1822, reference was made to 10 percent dividends in the context of poor purification procedure at the works.[224] In Drogheda, a Mr Downey argued in September 1890 that the corporation and private gas consumers should not be expected to bolster dividends at a time of increased charges for labour and coal. Likewise, with reference to expensive public lighting in Dungannon in 1899, Charles Knox clearly resented the fact that the gas company had been paying 10 percent dividends for the past few years.[225] At the time, Mr Dickson, the secretary of the Dungannon gas company, had assured all present that the gas company was not a philanthropic body but a business which was determined and entitled to make profits. Be that as it may, with the progression of the twentieth century, company management became increasingly conscious of the power of internal and external popular opinion, with company profits being adversely affected by the competitive designs of improved technology, advancing labour organisation and active nationalism. In effect, survival became increasingly difficult for an Irish industry deeply rooted in British expertise and dependent upon foreign exports of increasingly expensive raw material.

132

Coke, a by-product of gasmaking, was widely sold by Dublin Gas Company under the brand name ALCO. Here, the coke is being loaded for packaging.

Chapter 4

Challenges,
Change and Competition

In May 1860, while promoting T.L. Merriott's *Gas Consumer's Manual* explaining the simple practicalities of the 1859 Gas Measurement Act, *The Irish Times* printed the view that 'The position of the gas companies towards the consumers is not a fair one ... the late inquiries into the various systems of the metropolitan companies are sufficient to show that gas companies are not of the angelic host and that if they can turn a dishonest penny they will'.[1] Similarly, in January 1878, while advertising the schedule of the 1871 Gas Works Clauses Act, *The Downpatrick Recorder* declared that 'Gas companies enjoy what is practically a monopoly'.[2]

The view that consumers were at the mercy of company dictates was widespread. There were several courses open to disgruntled citizens with sufficient organisational abilities to pursue their grievances. They could abstain from using gas, as they did in Carlow, Naas, Enniskillen, Drogheda, and Portadown. They could oppose legislative moves by gas companies for extended powers as happened in Derry, Dungannon, and Lisburn.[3-10] They could acquire the management of the offending gas works in question as in Newry.[11] Alternatively, they could support or found rival companies for the sale of cheap gas as in Carlow in 1846, or Newtownards in 1870.[12]

Undoubtedly, there were legitimate reasons for public complaint. Most opposition sprang from the simple fact that gas prices were not uniform, being dependent to a large extent on the geographic and demographic nature of the relevant market place and excused for the most part by the price of coal. In 1898, for instance, gas charges varied considerably for what was perceived to be the same product.

Few critics bothered to acquire comparative statistics to a standard customary in British parliamentary proceedings, related to gas prices.

134

Price of gas per 1,000 Cubic feet

	lighting	engines or cooking
Armagh	3s. 9d.	3s. 4d.
Bandon	4s. 7d.	3s. 9d.
Clonmel	5s. 0d.	5s. 0d.
Cork	3s. 4d.	2s. 8d.
Drogheda	4s. 2d.	3s. 9d.
Dublin	3s. 8d.	3s. 5d.
Dundalk	4s. 2d.	3s. 6½d.
Enniskillen	5s. 0d.	4s. 0d.
Fermoy	4s. 2d.	4s. 2d.
Galway	5s. 6d.	4s. 6d.
Kilkenny	5s. 9d.	3s. 4d.
Limerick	4s. 4½d.	3s. 2½d.
Portrush	5s. 10d.	4s. 2d.
Queenstown	4s. 9d.	3s. 9d.
Skibbereen	5s. 0d.	3s. 6d.
Sligo	4s. 2d.	2s. 9d.
Tipperary	6s. 8d.	4s. 0d; or 4s. 2d.
Tuam	6s. 0d.	5s. 0d.
Waterford	4s. 0d.	3s. 6d.
Wexford	3s. 0d.	2s. 9d. [13]

Naturally, there was a certain element of bargaining involved in public acrimony. In Bagnalstown, in 1898, for instance, the town commissioners offered £40 to Mr Anderson for public lighting, whereupon he refused to do it for anything less than £60, the price they had paid Mrs McGrath more than three years previously. Eventually, both parties agreed to a contract for £50, the same contract price for the previous year and the one to which both parties had originally aspired.[14] In 1928, *The Ballina Herald* expressed the view that while the gas manager, Mr Reid, was entitled to strike a bargain the urban council was duty bound to do so.[15] Certainly, the game was carried too far in some cases. In Navan in 1908 the gas company stated that it had laid mains at Butterstream at cost price, with fitters' time being 7s. 6d. per day, and using 132 lengths of pipe costing 4s.0d. per length. After the gas committee discovered that the fitters' wages amounted to 5s. 10d. each per day and that the relevant pipes cost 3s.0d. per length, it began seriously to consider the prospects of electric lighting.[16]

Some companies asked for trouble by being less than diplomatic. In Dungannon in 1899 the company invited opposition to a provisional order allowing it to triple its share capital, by increasing the charge for public lighting on the principle that as the 3ft. burners were not governor burners they should be regarded as 4ft. burners because of the increased pressure involved in having the lamps positioned above the level of the gasworks.[17]

During the 1880s, the Dublin Alliance and Consumers' Company met (and survived) adverse commentary from public repres- entatives and even from company directors![18] Little wonder that *The Journal of Gas Lighting, Water Supply and Sanitary Improvement* observed that 'It seems to be the fate of the Dublin Company to be the object of ceaseless attacks',[19] while continuing to stress the Irishness of the company and its honest efforts to please those whom it served.[20] However, other companies were fortunate in maintaining a more dominant position. This was illustrated in Portadown in 1899 when it was admitted that 'one cannot force the hand of the gas company',[21] and in Kildare when it was noted with some regret that the company had simply failed to pay the stipulated fines for twenty-nine offences related to the proper attendance of the public lamps.[22] Clearly, the status and strength of gas companies varied from place to place and from time to time.

NEW ALTERNATIVES

Gradually, the bargaining strength of gas companies dwindled with the growth of alternative modes of power. In May 1878 James Kirby declared that is was pleasing to know that the ratepayers in provincial towns 'can now be relieved from those excessive charges for public lighting – from the annoyance given by such charges, and the inferior light emitted from the imperfectly purified gas supplied to their public lamps'[23] through the efforts of Messrs Whittle and Son, Whitehaven, in devising the gas oil lamp. These lamps were used to light the steam-boat pier and streets of Monkstown, Co. Cork, and were

> well adapted to meet the requirements of localities where gas cannot be manufactured, at a reasonable price. Oil sufficient for 40 hours' use is contained in an air-tight cistern surrounding the breast of the lamp and descends by a pipe to the interior of it. The oil is admitted in the same way as gas to an ingeniously-constructed burner where it is volatilised and burns steadily, emitting a light equal to about 25 standard candles at a cost of one farthing per hour. It can be regulated to give a lesser light, and, after being lighted, required no further attention; further, they can be fitted to existing lamp pillars.

By 1907, there was an array of alternatives to be found in Carrickfergus when it came to the question of public lighting.[24] Tenders for the lighting of the streets for three years were received from the Carrickfergus Gas Company, three electricity companies, one vaporised petrol company, and one oil gas company.[25] Similarly, the lighting of Whitehead (Co. Antrim) was contested by two acetylene companies and one oil gas company, with consideration being given to the founding of small coal gas works. The Sunbeam Company would supply an acetylene gas plant for £1,326 3s. 4d. or £1,441 3s. 4d.; Messrs Smyth Bros. of Great Patrick Street, Belfast, would do it for £1,650, and the Mansfield (Oil Gas) Company for £2,640.[26] Interestingly enough, it was estimated that it would cost £3,000 to light the town with coal gas, to say nothing of the appointment of a manager at £80 per annum and the employment of one or two stokers at £1 per week.

The Sunlight Gas Co. and Acetylene Lighting

The Sunlight Gas Company of Wellington Quay, Dublin, had little difficulty in arguing that acetylene gas was cheaper, brighter, safer, healthier and cleaner than coal gas.

> From a hygienic point of view, Sunlight Gas is superior to any other artificial light with the exception, perhaps, of Electricity against which it may be remarked that it is more economical, equally clean, and gives a softer and more pleasant light. Apart from increased illumination obtained, it is superior to coal gas in that it consumes less oxygen and evolves less heat. The light is steady and pleasing, and has not the greenish hue of incandescent gas light. . . . If a leakage were caused by a defective pipe, the rates at which the gas is diffused would naturally depend on the specific gravity, and as coal gas has a specific gravity of 0.4 as compared with 0.9 in acetylene gas, it would diffuse at the rate of three volumes of gas to two of acetylene. Owing to the penetrating and peculiar pungent smell of the gas, the least escape is at once detected and there is consequently less danger of explosions from leakage than from coal gas, and further, coal gas may be leaking in small quantities insufficient for detection, yet, it is being inhaled by the occupants of an apartment, and is deleterious to health, whilst the smallest escape in our gas is at once detected.[27]

Acetylene gas, formed from the chemical reaction of calcium carbide and water, was by no means a new product. In the early 1820s, while experimenting in the chemical laboratory of the Royal Dublin Society, Edmund Davy discovered what he called 'klumene'. As Davy did not pursue his investigations into the new hydro-carbon with sufficient vigour, however, it remained practically unknown until M. Berthelot rediscovered the gas and gave it the name acetylene. Indeed, the new gas only gained commercial possibilities with M. Wilson's new, easy method of producing calcium carbide, in large quantities, by subjecting a powdered mixture of lime and carbon to the powerful heat of an electric furnace, in 1888. Moreover, its commercial progress would have been more rapid were it not for the fact that hard graphite carbon became deposited on the burners before the employment of Goodwin's patented system. This system enabled the troublesome impurities to be devoured by generating a small proportion of carbonic acid gas simultaneously and in the same cylinder with the acetylene gas.

The work of the Sunlight Gas Company heralded the adoption of acetylene in Germany, Hungary, France and America. The company was particularly interested in those urban and rural areas which could not afford electricity or coal gas and could secure loans from the local government board for thirty years at 3¼ percent for the express purpose of erecting works of this nature. Because the action of water on carbide was simple compared with the elaborate works necessary for the distillation of gas from coal and the purification of the same, the process required the attendance of but one man and the company could afford to supply their product at an average cost of 3s. 9d. per 1,000 feet. Small companies supplying coal gas could not compete with this rate. Certainly, in Tanderagee, Co. Down, some forty-five years after the erection of a gasworks by Messrs Edmundson & Co., Dublin, and the celebration of the same with a lively fireworks display, it was admitted in 1908 that acetylene was cheaper than coal gas.[28] As early as 1902 acetylene was seen to have its advantages, and was adopted by certain firms in Nenagh,[29] Hillsborough, Ballymena and Dundalk.[30] In that year John Lemon & Son challenged one critic of acetylene to a competitive display between equal strengths of coal and acetylene gas whereby the loser would donate £50 for the benefit of the county infirmary![31]

Certainly, the Sunlight Gas Company was quick to defend the advantages of acetylene. On 18 September 1899, for instance, upon reading in *The Gas World* that six lamps were to be lighted by means of oil in Dungannon, the secretary of the company, Mr Heney, wrote to the relevant town clerk to draw his attention to the company's system of acetylene gas lighting which they had recently introduced into Dunfanaghy, Co. Donegal, and 'a large number of districts throughout the country'.[32]

Gas companies were more concerned with the growing threat from electricity, however, and not without reason. Following 'unreasonable' gas company demands in Dungannon in 1899, for instance, the immediate response of public representatives was to discuss the relative merits of founding or supporting two competing gas companies in 1897,[33] and the fact that the acquisition of the gasworks by the town representatives in Sligo was dismissed in 1899,[34] the formation of an electricity company seemed likely. Consideration had in fact been given to the possibility of electric lighting in Dungannon as early as 1885,[35] as it had in Tuam in 1887, Ennis in 1891 and Cobh in 1892.[36]

Competition from electricity, when it did come, hardly came as a surprise. As early as October 1848 *The Drogheda Conservative Journal* informed its readers of the invention of new electric light and warned the gas companies to 'look out'.[37] There was little doubt about the seriousness of the situation some thirty years later. In 1878, *The Downpatrick Recorder*, for instance, noticed the sudden drop in healthy gas shares in Bristol with news of Thomas Edison's invention of the electric lamp.[38] The inevitable challenge had to be met and faced with confidence, ingenuity, and tact. During the early days there was little difficulty in doing so and between 1882 and 1908 the number of gasworks in the United Kingdom rose from 352 to 491. In 1878 James Stelfox, manager in Belfast, stressed that all calculations submitted to the public regarding the relative costs of electricity and gas lighting were based on a theoretical estimate of the effective value of a single set of machinery which would be subject to considerable wear and tear, and that little serious attention should be paid to unsupported assertions by prejudiced advocates of the new system.[39] He believed that 'there can be no doubt that the present feeling of alarm among those interested in gas securities will call forth increased energy on the part of those whose duty it is to provide the public with lighting'.[40] Indeed, he predicted that an increased demand for gas lighting would follow a reduction in price brought about by the more extensive use of gas for heating and power purposes. In simple terms, then, he thought that the industry had nothing to fear because it had already changed.

James Stelfox was not the only one with a positive view of the industry's future, at the time. William Wallace, Fellow of the Royal Society of Engineers, declared in 1879 that he had no fear that gas interests would suffer in consequence of the electric light for many, many years.[41] He believed that at worst gas would be used side-by-side with electricity as long as coal could be got to produce it, and that if the production of gas decreased appreciably, the value of the by-products (benzole, anthracene, tar-oils, pitch and ammonia) would compensate through their relative scarcity and increasing value. More significantly, perhaps, he was 'very sanguine that gas lighting, during the next thirty years, will be developed to an extent to which we can at present form no adequate idea'.[42]

Both Stelfox and Wallace were correct in believing that the diversity of its usages and improvement of its transmission would allow gas to compete effectively with electricity. Furthermore, the industry had an initial advantage. While they may have resented or opposed the idea of 'monopolists' in theory, corporations and urban councils did not welcome the idea of additional disturbers ruthlessly rooting-up innocent and costly pavements to serve their needs.[43] As *The Portadown*

News observed, the wiring of a house was more awkward and costly than the putting down of gas pipes.[44] Indeed, in any event, the gas engine was by far the most economical and suitable machine for giving the required power for the production of electricity at the time.

In 1881, on the principle that gas lighting was superior to the best produced by electricity, the Directors of the Alliance and Dublin Consumers' Gas Company offered to light 'the classic precincts of Sackville Street and College Green', at their own expense, with electric lamps of the most approved type and to surrender responsibility for them to the corporation on condition that it supply the site and nominate the staff.[45] The city corporation was naturally surprised, and typically divided, on the merits of this novel approach by a gas company, but eventually agreed to the arrangement. Following the liquidation of the Dublin Electric Light Company founded in 1881 the gas company claimed that it was legally entitled to provide artificial light of any sort and applied for a provisional order under the 1882 Act. This was opposed by the corporation which cherished similar ambitions. But the gas company managed to secure permission from the Board of Trade to spend money on purposes unrelated to its gas business and built a new power house in Hawkins Street to supply customers in the Grafton Street, George's Street and Henry Street areas.[46] In providing electricity, then, the Dublin gas company succeeded where, for instance, others in Waterford and Cork failed.[47]

Serious concern about competition from electricity became evident in Cork as early as 26 November 1881 when Denny Lane called the attention of the directors of the gas company to several notices in *The Freeman's Journal* of 19 November stating that several electric light companies sought various parliamentary powers to open the streets, and to a subsequent letter from Mr Cotton in Dublin to the effect that the gas companies should take joint action against the grant of such powers as they were altogether without precedent.[48] It was considered unwise to take expensive legal action.[49]

Dr O'Sullivan alleged in January 1882 that the loss of pressure in Leanders' Quay was due to an excessive consumption of 5 cubic feet of gas per lamp in Patrick Street in order 'to blind the public to the progress of electric lighting!'[50] Nevertheless, with his first-hand experience of Siemens' regenerative gas lamps and the incandescent mantle, to say nothing of more modern techniques of production and treatment of gas,[51] Denny Lane was confident that gas proprietors had nothing to fear from electricity.[52] It was, as *The Journal of Gas Lighting* observed, a great advantage to the directors of the company to be able to rely on a secretary who took positive pleasure in keeping abreast of scientific progress, when faced with 'matters commonly garbled in the daily newspapers'.[53]

Denny Lane, d. 1895. Lane was the only child of a wealthy Cork distiller. He was one of the Young Ireland poets and a friend of Thomas Davis, Charles Gavin Duffy and John Blake Dillon. He was managing director of the Cork Gas Company for many years and President of the Institute of Gas Engineers.

Trained in law, gifted in verse, and innovative in private enterprise,[54] Denny Lane became well known in the British gas industry as the humorous Irishman who felt obliged to preside over the Gas Institute in London in 1886, in order 'to maintain law and order over a body which consisted chiefly of Englishmen and Scotsmen'![55] Furthermore, he revealed the quality of his mind in a lengthy, but nonetheless interesting, letter objecting to the granting of a provisional order by the Board of Trade to the Irish House-to-House Electricity Company for the lighting of Cork, in January 1890. He wrote:

> The Irish House-to-House Electricity Co. is one of a large number of similar companies started at the time. Of these, twelve proposed to raise a capital of £100,000 each, and each had the same subscribers to the Articles of Association. Mr R. Hammond of 117 Bishopsgate Street E.C. and Mr H. Linklater of the same address Accountant being two of the number and the other 5 Subscribers all residing in London one being a Chemist, another an electrical Engineer, another a Clerk, another a Civil Engineer while the remaining Subscriber is described as Gentleman.
>
> Before the 1st of July last, the Electricity Company applied to the Corporation to sanction their application to the Board of Trade and their representatives wrote to the Corporation stating that 'The Company is an Irish one and will be managed by a Board of Directors composed by Irish Gentlemen and having their Chief Office in Dublin'.
>
> So far as I have been able to ascertain the above statement is *not* correct. The Company is not an Irish one, application has been made for the names of Irish Directors but I have not been able to ascertain one single name and the Chief and only office as mentioned in the draft Provisional Order is at 15 St. Helen's Place in the City of London. It is submitted that this is a material matter, and that no order should under the circumstances be granted to the Promoters.

The core of Denny Lane's argument was that

> Under the 15th and other clauses of the Draft Order the Electric Company seek for power to interfere with the pipes and mains of the Gas Company. If, on doing so, damage ocurred to said mains causing leakage of Gas, such leakage could cause damage to the Gas Company and by explosion or otherwise might cause loss of life or health and other injuries. If an escape of Gas took place into the arched main sewers already referred to and, there mixing with air, formed an explosive mixture which was fired by an Electric spark a disastrous explosion might occur on account of the large area of these ancient arched Channels. As the Electric Company has no office in Ireland, any company or persons sustaining damage would be obliged to prosecute their suit in England, having to give security for costs, and become liable for costs of witnesses, etc., for the cause of actions arising in Ireland.

The Electric Company seek in the first instance to lay their mains only in the streets included in the Second Schedule. These streets, while being the most important in the city, are only one and three quarters miles in length while the gas company are obliged to keep a constant supply of Gas at a certain pressure in mains between 60 and 70 miles in length. In some portions, there is little more consumption than that arising from the public lamps which are placed at distances of 65 yards and over, and from which the Company receives an annual payment of only £2 1s. 7d. per lamp, although the columns, lamps and fittings are provided by the Company. In many districts the inhabitants are very poor, and use little or no gas. It would be unjust to the Gas Company that their rivals should pick out the richer part of the city and incur no obligation to supply the poorer portion. If Electricity were employed to a considerable extent in the best paying portion of the city, the natural consequence would be an enhanced cost of all illumination in the poorer portion.

The local taxation of Cork is extremely high, generally exceeding in the aggregate 10s. 0d. in the Pound. To this, the Gas Company is by far in the largest contributor, paying generally about £2,500 a year. The heaviest part of their valuation is on the easement of laying mains, and this is based on the profits of the Company. If such profits were diminished by the competition of the Electric Light the valuation to the rates would be diminished. The effect would be that either the rates or the cost of Gas would be raised. It is believed that the demand for the Electric Light would not be sufficient to produce assessable profits which would compensate the rate-payers for the loss above mentioned . . .

The Electric Light being at the price proposed far dearer than gas may be called a light of luxury – a light for the rich – and the effect of its introduction would be to raise the cost of illumination for the public in general, and the rise would fall most severely upon the humbler classes who are least able to bear it.[56]

He further argued that this British electricity company sought to snatch a concession, without apparent capital or substantial guarantee and with intent to sell it to some other body with capital. Indeed, he believed that 'In the present unsettled state of Electrical questions it would be better to defer for some time the determination of a system of supply which no one in Cork demands', as 'the supply of gas is unfailing and the illuminating power much above the Parliamentary Standard and it would be better, in the interest of all except company promoters, to wait for further experience before substituting for a satisfactory mode of illumination another which is precarious, imperfectly developed and to a certain extent in the experimental stage.'

In January 1890, Denny Lane opposed electric lighting in Cork because ordinary methods of insulation would be inoperative in some streets where water came up to the kerb stones in high tides with salt water damaging the insulation for high-tension mains. However, due to growing interest in the question of electric lighting on the part of the city corporation, and advice from Mr Tratter (editor of the *Electrician* newspaper) and W. Crompton (an electrical engineer in London), he supported the view that electric lighting would be more successful in the hands of gas companies than any other body as they could work it more economically. Moreover, he was successful in converting the directors of the company to this particular idea, and in August 1891 *The Journal of Gas Lighting* reported that 'the directors of the Cork Gas Consumers' Company have decided, with the concurrence of the shareholders, to apply to the Board of Trade for an electric lighting order on grounds that it could supply the citizens with electricity cheaper than a special company, and that by distributing electricity by means of gas engines they could obtain profit in this way'.[57] The journal itself did not share this view and declared, in no uncertain terms, that

> the gas directors do not expect to make anything by their proposed venture. They cannot even pretend that Cork is a particularly favourable scene for operations of this nature; and therefore why they want to embark in anything of the kind passes comprehension. They cite foreign examples; but they must know that foreign gas companies can do what they like with their capital, which is not the case with any British statutory company. Not one percent of these adventurous concerns make money by their electric lighing departments. . . . Altogether, the project of the Cork Gas Directors appears to us ill advised. They had far better stick to their own business and let those who like it lose money over electric lighting.

Obviously, the journal had no confidence in the profitability of electric lighting. In any event, the Cork Gas Consumers' Company failed in its repeated efforts to secure the right to supply electricity to Cork at this time.

A Slow Start

With the widespread adoption of incandescent lighting at the turn of the century, and increased awareness of the value of regulators and governors in maintaining profitable pressure levels, there was little to fear from electricity companies.[58] Despite numerous breakages of delicate incandescent mantles,[59] electric lighting did not overtake gas lighting in popular estimation for another three decades. In Carlow, the first provincial town to adopt electricty in 1891, only fourteen of the 103 patrons of the local gas company had adopted the new medium by 1892.[60] In Keady in 1908, the urban council saw fit to continue using gas and formed a new company, even though the old one, founded in 1851, had been so unsuccessful that it had offered the council the badly situated works and deficient pipes free of charge—and it had never paid dividends to its shareholders![61]

In Navan, the lighting committee of the corporation, in 1908, recommended that information be obtained from Carlow, Manorhamilton, Drumshambo and Carrick-on-Shannon regarding the merits of electricity as these towns were about the same size as their own.[62] However, no immediate decision was taken and in 1911, further information was elicited from Enniscorthy, Tralee, Boyle, Limerick, Bray, Pembroke, Derry, Carlow, Rathmines, Dundalk, Kildare, Waterford, Carrick-on-Shannon, Ballyclare and Killarney regarding the viability of electricity.[63] Again, no immediate decision was taken. In 1919 more information about the supply of electricity by local private companies was received from Birr, Nenagh (where the gas company intended to supply electricity), Naas and Kildare, and yet only in September 1921 did the town of Navan completely abandon the use of gas for public lighting.[64] In other words, the quality and cost of gas lighting in Navan was sufficiently competitive with electricity or oil to survive thirteen years of occasional scrutiny.

Naturally, the pending presence of such competition had some effect. On 8 December 1888, only a week after a public discussion on a Mr Perry's offer to provide electric lighting in Galway, the gas company there made a reduction of 1s. 9d. per 1,000 feet in order to make it the cheapest rate of gas supply of any town in the west of Ireland.[65] In some places electricity was connected with modernism and displaced gas of whatever quality or cost, as suggested by Denny Lane's opening remarks in his inaugural address on the merits of gas and electricity at the thirtieth annual meeting of the Incorporated Gas Institute in Belfast in June 1893.

> 'Once upon a time there was a king and he had three sons', so begin scores of fairy tales; and gas, the iron-way, and electricity are the three "Princes of the blood" whom the nineteenth century has engendered. I need not tell you that the eldest was, and is, according to the story tellers the worst of characters; the second middling; and the youngest a paragon of all the virtues.

Denny Lane pointed to the fact that Carlow, with its steadily declining population of nine thousand inhabitants, could scarcely afford to pay the rent and salaries involved in the production of electricity; that Waterford, one of the wealthiest municipalities in the kingdom and an important port where several lines of railway converge and with a population three times that of Carlow, had abandoned electric lighting; and that the Larne Corporation had refused to take over the electricity plant there upon the death of J.E.H. Gordon. Gas lighting, of course, was to a large extent doomed as a commercial venture. In Lurgan, in 1905 for instance, E. Lane confessed his belief that, with three hundred mantles, Lurgan was the best 'lit' town in the country. However, while no-one exactly condemned the quality of gas lighting, no-one defended the gas company from H.G.

McGrath's speculative criticism that 'the lighting of the town would never be satisfactorily undertaken until the council had it in their own hands', and that 'electric lighting would well repay the ratepayers of Lurgan'.[66] In Coleraine in 1924 it was admitted that the price of gas was the third lowest in Ireland and of excellent quality, but would remain so only if the demand for gas did not increase and thereby necessitate big expenditure in providing a new retort house.[67] Between 1904 and 1924, the output of gas had increased from 17,000,000 to 33,000,000 cubic feet of gas because of urban development and expansion. Rapid urban expansion and sharp technological competition spelt the ruin of many gas companies. However, it is probably true to say that most were the victims of political and social unrest during the twentieth century.

SOCIAL AND POLITICAL INFLUENCE

Certainly, the industry had always been conscious of social and political factors during the late nineteenth and early twentieth centry. In Cork, with the significant tailor's strike of 1870, the Royal Irish Constabulary occupied the gasworks but failed to prevent the quenching of the public lamps and resultant adoption of French revolutionary techniques described briefly as follows:

> Academy Street . . . was then quite dark, and the police were unable to discern the source whence the stones proceeded. They were got into order, and directed to rush down and clear the street. Here, however, was first discovered one of the most desperate features of the disturbances, for before the police had proceeded far in their charge the first ranks tumbled over a barricade of floats that had been erected across the street. The whole line was thrown into disorder, and the party who defended the barricade kept up a desperate fire upon the discomfitted assailants. A troop of cavalry were at the same time approaching at a gallop, and the danger was that in the darkness that prevailed they would ride over the police and find themselve precipitated over the unlooked-for obstruction. Fortunately Mr Egan had time to keep back the cavalry, and then he sought to remedy the confusion that was caused in his ranks. His men were got into order, and in short time they removed the barricade, but up to the last moment they were assailed with stones from the parties who erected it. Yet, when they rushed to capture some prisoners from among those who introduced this French method of fighting, they found they were somewhere else.[68]

In contrast, attempts to incorporate the Dundalk Gas Company with the third reading of a Bill in the British House of Commons in 1886 failed because 'The Nationalist members seized upon this insignificant measure as a convenient test of their power, and made such a fuss over it that the Government were induced to abandon the Select Committee and vote against the Bill. The fierce followers of Mr Parnell alleged all sorts of misdoings on the part of the unfortunate Dundalk Gas Company as reasons why they should not be incorporated with statutory rights; but the greatest wrong in connection with the measure which the House was asked to resent was the fact that it had been considered by a Select Committee of four members not one of whom was an Irishman'.[69] Also, there was some awareness of international factors as in Clonmel in response to a letter from Bruce Anderson to the effect that the coming year's supply of coal should be contracted for immediately in view of the probability of war between Russia and Japan in 1904.[70] These incidents related to outside interference in the day-to-day accumulation of capital and production of gas were mild when compared with those faced during the twentieth century in the context of growing competition from electricity and oil.

If one ignores the take-overs or amalgamations in Dublin, Carlow, Cork, Clonmel, Wexford, Newtownards, Limerick, Lisburn, Cookstown, Downpatrick and Dungarvan, between 1823 and 1897, the following graph suggests that the trend towards closure began some time before the invention of the tungsten electric lamp in 1910 and the outbreak of the First World War in 1914. However, the war did have considerable impact on the industry in Ireland, with severe restrictions on coal and increased rates for transportation of the same. In Wexford, in 1916 for instance, it was decided to postpone the extension of the number of retorts 'owing to the present extraordinary circumstances caused by the Great European War, such as the unusually high prices for nearly all things', and the high freights of 16s. 0d. per ton from the Mersey district as compared with 4s. 6d. to 5s. 0d. at the same time of year in the years immediately preceeding the outbreak of hostilities.[71] A year later, it was resolved that the citizens of Wexford be made aware of the fact that 'henceforth there can be no extension made to the number of existing lights, no new customers will be supplied, nor can boiling rings, cookers, or heating stoves extra to those at present in use be permitted, and there will be no supply to gas engines beyond those at present in use'.[72] Business, presumably, would continue as normal after the war.

However, this did not always happen, as suggested by the situation which developed in Newtownards. Here, it was recalled in 1918 that the manager, Mr Roberts, 'had for many weeks to keep on a chair in the gas works for three or four nights a week' and that after one thirty-six hour spell of trying to produce sufficient gas for the town his health had completely broken down so that, after seventeen and a half years of dedicated service, he had tendered his resignation for medical reasons.[73] Roberts was replaced by Mr Scott who saw the need to replace the damaged horizontal carbonising plant, installed in 1901, with a carburetted water-gas plant. This, however, failed

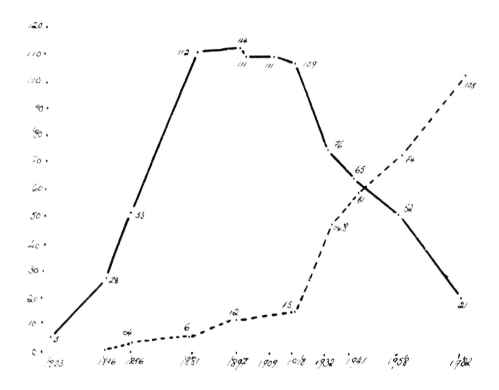

The rise and fall of the Gas Manufacturing Industry in Urban Centres throughout Ireland,
1822 – 1982.

to bring down the price of gas from the 8s. 0d. per 1,000 cubic feet charged during the war, to avert a strike by the men at the works, or produce an efficient supply of gas by anticipating coal shortages in the following three years.[74] Naturally, some of the citizens could not help resenting the fact that their old manager, who now controlled the gasworks in Donaghadee, could more than satisfy the citizens there through the utilisation of the old plant which he had purchased from Newtownards, while their new manager and new gas committee could only make excuses for their obvious short-comings![75] Indeed, the situation was so serious that the gas committee elected to include all council members on the supposition that 'when there is a few on the committee, everyone is responsible but, when the whole council acts on a committee, no one is responsible'![76]

THE AFTERMATH OF THE GREAT WAR

The problems endured by the industry during the war were discussed at the thirtieth annual general meeting of the Irish Association of Gas Managers in Dublin in August 1918. Here, H. Kirkham, from New Ross, stressed the significant role played by the gas industry in the overall war effort by quoting Lord Moulton's comments to the Institution of Gas Engineers regarding the invaluable use of by-products like benzol, toloul and ammonia in furnishing the materials for high explosives, and adding that 'our industry . . . ' has also provided heat for annealing shells, cooking and hot water in canteens, the propulsion of vehicles, and other services in war work'. After thereby patting the industry on the back for 'such service in upholding the stability of the empire' he then directed his attention to those in authority who, despite the cooperative efforts of the industry, hampered its progress by allowing the price of sulphuric acid to increase while refusing to allow the price of sulphate of ammonia to rise in proportion, and by creating a shortage of coal in Ireland while shipping coal to neutral countries. His views were shared to some extent by Messrs Saville (Drogheda), Anderson (London) and Paterson (Waterford). While recognising the increased cost of labour and acid, Mr Saville thought it unfair that 'an English manufacturer of sulphate, sending it to Ireland, got an allowance for carriage; but those who made it in Ireland, and with carriage to pay on coal, and in many cases on the acid as well, received no allowance'. Mr Anderson did not think that the production of sulphate of ammonia was not as important as the coal situation because it only concerned the larger works, but considered that the Board of Trade's reading of the Coal Price Limitation Act was ludicrous.

> in the Coal Price Limitation Act it was stated that the price should be 4s. 0d. per ton above pre-war rates. Any common-sense person reading this, would take it

to mean that, if he had been paying 12s. 0d. before, he should be charged 16s. 0d.; but what was the Board of Trade reading of the Act? If some person instead of paying 12s. 0d. per ton, had been paying 20s. 0d. that man would have to pay 24s.0d. and everybody else who had been buying a similar quantity of coal had his price put up to 24s. 0d.

Mr Paterson noted that 'when the scarcity of petrol first came about, and users of traction power looked around for a substitute, they could find no better or cheaper one than coal gas, but immediately they hit upon this fact, the authorities, in their wisdom, put a stop to its use', with the resultant hardship on the industry. Clearly, the speakers felt ill done by, and not without some justification.

Between 1914 and 1929, twenty-five gas companies – supplying over four thousand customers with upwards of ninety million cubic feet of gas per annum – closed down.[77] Of these small gasworks, at least nine did so owing to inability to pay for coal during the war. Between 1914 and 1929, increased costs affecting coal averaged about 68 percent, while those related to freights averaged about 20 percent and would have been higher but for the depressed state of the market. Coupled with these increases were losses sustained through the adoption of the Summer Time Act, the shorter hours generally kept by shopkeepers and the use of Greenwich Time; the closing of some military barracks and the resultant evaporation of finances secured, directly or indirectly in the Free State through foreign occupation before independence; the founding of numerous electricity companies; and the raising of wages in accordance with inflation heralded by the war. In Cork, for instance, 'war wages' in October 1917 involved an increase of 3s. 6d. per week for manual workers and 5s. 0d. per week for clerical workers.[78] These increases were further added to in May, October and November of 1918, while in March 1926 the question of reducing such wages was postponed indefinitely for obvious reasons.[79]

Moreover, the First World War must also have brought a certain disruption in day to day staff relations as suggested by the following ruling in Cork in May 1915 that the secretary of the company be authorised

to add the name of the Company to the list of signatures for Cork Recruiting Committee to the resolution [that]: 'We the undersigned recognizing that our very existence as a free people depends upon our services in the war hereby undertake as far as possible to reinstate at its conclusion those men in our employment who volunteer for service at the front. Where through change caused by the war the position is gone or the returning employee is incapacitated for his former post, we hope jointly to interest ourselves on his behalf.'[80]

150

Indeed, the Great War, which effectively demolished the remnants of the old aristocratic order in Europe, had ideological repercussions that were felt in Ireland and could hardly be ignored by the gas industry, given the noteworthy experience of H.L. Adams, manager of the Tipperary Gas Works, in negotiating wage agreements and attempting to define the status and position of fitters and casual labourers.

On 4 March 1922 the workers at Tipperary Gas Works simply took over the plant, barred the manager from entering the company's premises, raised the red flag and elected a formerly dismissed employee, C. Heffernan, as manager.[81] At the time of takeover, they had a plentiful supply of coal with which to produce gas and satisfy local residents. Accordingly, they did not concern themselves unduly with the somewhat embarrassing problem of charging for the gas supplied until the end of June when they proposed that the Urban District Council should supervise the collection of money deposited in the slot meters and consider taking over the works, as attempts at negotiation had failed and the owners of the company were English! Naturally, many customers continued to use gas while noting that if they should pay their gas bills to the new proprietors they might have to do so a second time when the works came into the possession of its owners. The workers hoped to by-pass this difficulty with the help of the Urban District Council which, like many more public bodies, was hardly known for its appreciation of gas rates struck by private enterprise at home or abroad. However, an indication of how disproportionate or unusual this departure was from normal strike proceedings was the fact that the terms dictated by the men during negotiations simply involved the status and wages of only one worker and a promise of permanent employment for two others.

Interestingly enough, the affair became something of an international incident, as the British company lost no time in informing the British government of its duty to influence the provisional government in Dublin to exercise its newly-acquired responsibility for the maintenance of law and order! A solution to the problem, however, was gained not through negotiation but through the extension of the civil war to Tipperary town. Treaty forces eventually took the gasworks from anti-treaty forces, so that the gas supply was restored by the first week of August 1923.

CIVIL STRIFE

The industry also suffered, to some extent, from the nationalist struggle following the 1916 Rising which secured limited independence for the southern twenty-six counties and surrendered the possibility of incorporating the other six counties to the future, and thereby culminated in the Irish Civil War. In Cork, for instance, the gas company suffered an immediate loss of £532 19s. 6d. in March 1921 through the burning by the 'Black and Tans' of Patrick Street and the resultant destruction of meters and rent.[82] In May 1922 and July 1925, company cars were stolen, while in October and December 1923 company officials were robbed by armed men on two occasions to the total tune of £94.[83] Indeed, in September 1923, it was noted that 755 panes of glass had been broken and 336 lamps destroyed during the month of August![84]

Nor was Cork gas company the only one to suffer as a result of nationalist frustrations. In February 1923 the exhauster in Tralee Gas Works was destroyed by armed men.[85] Moreover, the problems met in this regard were not always external as suggested by the following instance in Dundalk in August 1925. Here, a special meeting of the directors of the gas company was called to meet a deputation of townspeople who wished to have a collector for the company, Philip McGuillian, who had allegedly been imprisoned because of his prominence in the national movement, reinstated.[86] The deputation argued that McGuillian's securities had never been released by the board and that he had never been formally released from the collectorship, while stating that the Urban District Council insisted on his reinstatement to his former position. On behalf of the company, the chairman Mr Cox pointed out to the deputation that

1. No victimisation had occurred as McGuillian would not have been employed again, at the same pay, by the company.
2. McGuillian's position had been kept open for him for nine months and, as no limit was put on the duration of his internment, it was compulsory to appoint a new collector.
3. McGuillian, on being released, made no attempt to get reinstated and had to be sent for before he came back.
4. McGuillian never mentioned that he expected to be reinstated and actually congratulated the new collector (Mr Murphy) with the remark that he would like to see no one in the job better than Murphy.
5. No bond was released by the company as it had originally paid the fidelity bond for McGuillian out of its own purse.

When the deputation returned after a short discussion of these revelations, it was told that the collectorship would not be returned to McGuillian under any circumstances, but that the directors were willing to sanction an honorarium of £100 in recognition of his services. Thus, the company was left with H.F. Murphy, who hardly proved an ideal replacement as indicated by the fact that he was prosecuted for embezzlement in July 1926.[87]

The gas industry had reason to resent the new Irish governmental attitudes which threatened to sweep away British legislation related to the industry even before the ratification of the Anglo-Irish treaty. By January 1922, for instance, the Dáil Eireann Local Government Department had written to Fermoy and Waterford councils that gas companies should not take advantage of an English law to interfere with an Irish public body but should be prepared to leave the suggested system of charging to arbitration by a circuit judge appointed by the minister for home affairs.[88] Rates rose appreciably until Judge Doyle ruled in favour of the Dundalk Gas Company in 1929, which, interesting enough, had been supported in its legal test case by other gas companies.[89] In 1928, however, an Act was passed which compelled gas companies in the twenty-six counties to have all meters, which did not bear the Free State seal, re-stamped within five years of the date of the Act. The legislation may have had something to do with the poor repairs carried out on meters during the Second World War. Certainly, it did nothing to help gas companies distant from the testing or stamping sites, and in 1929 it was noted that 'electrical undertakings are under no liability to have their meters either tested or sealed officially'.

In 1929, with the Shannon hydro-electricity scheme nearing completion and being viewed as a positive national achievement, the situation for thirty of the remaining eighty-five gasworks seemed less then healthy. The problem of reduced sales, as W.L. Dalby of Wicklow, observed, at the thirty-seventh annual meeting of the Irish Association of Gas Managers in Dublin in 1929, was mainly confined to the southern states as 'the Northern works have improved their position very materially since the pre-war days . . . in an atmosphere more favourable to gas than . . . in the South'. Clearly, the approach to competition from electricity evident at this meeting was markedly different to that of 1918 when the then president of the Association, H. Kirkham, had announced to the delegates the fact that the directors of the New Ross gas company had sought powers to supply electricity in addition to gas, while expressing the view that 'There is no blinking the fact that the use of electricity is spreading . . . we are in the business to supply light, heat, and power; and . . . should . . . be in a position to give it to our customers in whichever way they prefer'. Most of the delegates present in 1918 obviously did not view serious competition from the young electricity industry as an immediate threat. Although M.J. Treacy from Wicklow 'could not see what advantage there was in introducing an electricity supply in connection with a gas works . . . to compete against themselves', most accepted Mr Paterson's 'if you're not in, you can't win' philosophy embodied in his argument that

Gas companies were in a better position than any other body to supply electric light cheaply. They could combine two businesses in a way that could lead

TRAILING HIS COAT!

Mr. George Anderson, president of the Irish Association of Gas Managers, in his presidential address at the annual meeting in Dublin this week, said that "like a popular beverage they were still going strong."

[Cartoon by Wallace Corp]

In 1939 the confidence and optimism of the gas industry in the face of ever-growing competition from electricity was perhaps slightly overstated in this cartoon from *The Gas World* of that year.

154

"HOLDING THE FORT!"

In his Presidential Address to the Irish Association of Gas Managers, Mr. Arnold Law said the Irish undertakings were holding the fort against competitors who were not subject to the same restrictions as themselves, and in many cases were increasing their sales.

[*Cartoon by Wallace Coop*]

The gas industry strikes back! Cartoon from *The Gas World*, August 1938.

to ... economy. ... They could not close their eyes to the fact that electricity was the popular light of the moment, and that communities would have it, if they could. Local authorities of ten embarked on electric light schemes which involved considerable loss; and every ratepayer had to share this loss. ... [Gas Companies] as the largest ratepayers, would have to subsidise their opponents. This was why they had thought of introducing it themselves.

COMMERCIAL REALITIES

By 1929 the situation had obviously changed, with government prejudiced in favour of the new industry, so that the president of the Gas Association advocated that the gas industry 'should adopt a far more aggressive attitude and indulge in a little boosting'.

As befitting his position as president, Mr Dalby was optimistic despite his awareness of impending adversity:

> Now that the Shannon Electricity Scheme is so far advanced, many of our members will soon be faced with competition from it. Some gas undertakings are bound to suffer considerably at first but the high charges which must be made generally to ensure the solvency of the scheme as a whole will deter many who might otherwise be disposed to adopt electricity for lighting. We need not fear serious competition for heating and cooking etc., as even the smallest gas companies can compete favourably for this business. I would impress upon all the necessity of pushing business in cooking and heating for we must rely on such business as cooking more and more in the future.

Highlighting advances related to gas cookers, water-heating appliances and gas fires, Dalby stressed the need 'to meet the loss of a part of our lighting load by extending sales in other directions'. W.H. Ainsworth, from Manchester, bolstered this positive approach to the future with proud memories of the not so distant past 'when coal was short and labour unobtainable except at a prohibitive price, ... when managers of even big works took off their coats and overcame their difficulties by the sweat of their brows' and when, in some cases, 'sawdust and tar were used to make gas' and in others 'gas was made from crude oil at the risk of life and limb.' He then alluded to the difficulty of obtaining assistants due to the diminished status of the industry, while advocating good advertising through the employment of a keen, energetic and courteous salesman, active sales through systematic research of local needs and potential, and prompt maintenance by well qualified fitters. This led to some discussion on the merits of courageously sinking profits in showrooms and exhibitions and to T.J. Reid's condemnation of the 'huge scheme of propaganda' started by the Electricity Supply Board. Reid was not slow to point out that the claim that electricity was the most economical fuel for lighting, heating, and power purposes was untrue, and made the perceptive remark that 'This was a national electricity scheme; and while they might imagine that the State would hold the balance evenly between the two industries, in this case . . . it would be too much to expect that the State would not try to advance their particular scheme to the disadvantage of the gas industry, if so allowed'. This fear was to gain resonance with time, especially under the first de Valera administration.

The situation did not improve after 1929, and the *Gas World* reported that between 1914 and 1934, 'no less than one third of the gas concerns in Ireland had gone out of business, partly because of difficulties in paying for the coal they must of necessity import, and partly because of the advent of state-aided electricity and similar super-imposed difficulties'.[90] In effect, this meant that thirty-seven works, involving a total annual output of over 140 million cubic feet of gas, had closed. There is little doubt but that the industry increasingly felt itself to be under siege from 1932 onwards.

In September 1932, Francis J. Dickens, chairman of the Alliance and Dublin Gas Company, complained to his shareholders of 'exceptional difficulty owing to legislative proposals and changes'. Import duties of 5s. 0d, a ton on British coal, and 20 percent on iron goods had been imposed on the industry in the name of self-sufficiency. The government had made concessions. Gas meters, for instance, were subject to import duties but the component parts required for their assembly in Ireland were not. Nevertheless, there was no escaping the fact that import duties on British coal would mean a loss of £39,000 with the carbonisation of 156,000 tons, and this could not be avoided as foreign coals did not yield as much gas and were expensive to procure. The company was faced with a dilemma which impeded positive progress, and Dickens argued that

> They could not possibly meet the additional cost entailed, especially as there were no offsetting advantages such as an increased yield of coke or tar, without either increasing the price of gas or reducing expenditure in some other direction. If the price of gas was increased, sales were unlikely to be maintained so the only tentative measure they could take was to cut down expenditure on work which, although highly desirable and necessary, was not of immediate and pressing importance, in the hope that when the position approached normality once more they would be able to undertake any accumulated arrear. . . . It was the earnest hope that an early settlement of the contentious matters existing between the two countries might be reached and thus permit the abolition of the emergency duties which were causing such difficulty and loss all round.[91]

Apparently, Dickens 'appreciated the action of the Government in meeting the demands of the industry in so far as it had done'. Within a year, his appreciation had wilted as he sorely resented the addition of 0s. 5½d. per therm of gas sold through importation duties, the imposition of the Corporation Profits Tax on gas companies despite their statutory obligations as a public service and limitations imposed on their prices and dividends under sliding-scale provisions and other factors, and unfair competition from foreign coke which could be imported duty free.[92]

THE 1930s

In 1932, there were seventy-six undertakings in existence – twenty-seven in Northern Ireland and forty-nine in the Free State – with an annual make of 9,010 million cubic feet of gas. To this, Belfast contributed 4,226 million, Dublin 2,413 million, Cork 438 million, Bangor 223 million, Derry 197 million, and Limerick 130 million.[93] As these were the six largest, the remaining seventy works produced an average of 19 million cubic feet of gas each, and did not individually exceed 130 million. Ireland, then, was essentially a country of small works whose destiny became increasingly dependent on political issues. Gasworks in the South were the first to suffer as a consequence of the severing of the imperial link between Britain and Ireland. The effect of the import duties was noticeable as suggested by the fact that between January and October 1932 only 90,194 cwt, of gas and water pipes (worth £63,304) were imported as compared with 205,196 cwt, of the same (worth (£118,851) for the corresponding period in 1931.[94] Indeed, it is hardly surprising that, in 1932, the president of the Gas Association, L.C. Young from Carlow, expressed the view that

> Gas undertakings should have more consideration from the Government and local authorities than they have had for, as well as paying rates and taxes, they give a lot of employment [outside the industry] in the way of freights. Also there are dock, railway and other charges to be paid . . . but for the gas industry considerably higher quantities of coal would have to be imported as coal burned in the raw state does not go anything like so far as when it is converted into gas. Also there are the by-products – coke, tar, sulphate of ammonia etc., which would have to be imported as a country could not exist without them.[95]

He predicted the possible closure of some small gasworks through the imposition of tariffs on essential imports of British goods, and explained that 'varying qualities of coal are required for different types of retorts and each undertaking must for that reason have free choice to select the most suitable grades'.

In 1935, the president of the Association, J.A. Rooney outlined governmental policy:

Up to the commencement of this year, we could buy coals from foreign countries at whatever price we could get for them without paying any customs duty on them, but if we bought British we had a customs duty of five shillings per ton to pay on them. Now we must buy British and pay the customs duty of 5s. 0d. per ton, and besides we are restricted to a quota . . . the transport and other industries where coal was an essential of the manufacturing process were getting their coal supplies free of duty. . . . Of course, we are fighting the E.S.B. with all our might and main; but we should not be the only party using large quantities of coal, to be victimised. . . . To add to our discomfort, in the Free State, the British and Northern Ireland governments have put an import duty of one penny per gal. on all our tar imported into them and prices are so low that they practically only pay the cost of exportation.[96]

He further pointed to the fact that no import duty had been placed on foreign bitument, used as an alternative to coal tar on Irish roads, while conceding the fact that coal tar was often blamed for the poisoning of fish due to 'the damp nature of the country and the proximity of the various rivers with the roads'.

The approach adopted by the southern government towards the industry was hardly regarded as favourable or fair, as suggested by a committee report from the Association in 1935 to the effect that

The continued imposition of 5s. 0d. per ton on all coals imported is a very heavy burden and no amount of correspondence seems to have any effect on the Ministry of Industry and Commerce. The quota system has hit us also, and the Government will only alter the amount they allow after continued efforts on behalf of each company that finds the amount too small for its requirements. Efforts are being made . . . to have the coal tarriff removed for gasworks (it being raw material for us) . . .[97]

Indeed, the committee in question brought the government's attention to the fact that some gasworks had little capacity left for crude tar because the amount of road tar used between 1932 and 1935 had fallen from 11,000 to 6300 tons with the free importation of bitumen.

DUBLIN VERSUS LONDON

The dispute between the Dublin and Westminster governments in July 1932, which resulted in importation duties on British goods into Ireland and Irish goods into Britain had been essentially political in origin. The newly elected Fianna Fáil government under Eamon de Valera had refused to transfer to Britain the annuities paid by Irish farmers to redeem the financial assistance advanced to them under various pre-independence land acts. Britain reacted with a forcefulness which surprised de Valera. After all, the

Alderman Alfred (Alfie) Byrne, Lord Mayor of Dublin, arriving at Jury's Hotel with the President of the Irish Association of Gas Managers, P.J. MacEvoy (Midleton, Co. Cork) for the opening of the annual meeting in August 1936.

annual sum of £5 million involved, though adding considerably to Free State revenue, represented less than 0.6 percent of total British government revenue.[98] Arguing that the Fianna Fáil government was reneging on an obligation clearly recognised by previous Irish governments, and suspecting that de Valera intended to undermine the Anglo-Irish treaty of 1922, the Westminster government attempted to cripple the Free State economy by imposing duties on Irish agricultural produce, and thereby shepherd Irish electoral consciousness in the direction of the more moderate Cumann na nGaedheal. In response to the resultant plight suffered by Irish farmers, de Valera pushed the theory of self-sufficiency, increased taxation to support export bounties on Irish agricultural produce, and availed of 1931 protectionist legislation to impose duties on imports of British coal, cement, electrical goods, iron and steel manufactures and sugar. This action hurt Ireland's economy more than that of her immediate neighbour. However, from 1935 the situation began to improve as a result of a succession of coal-cattle pacts – which exchanged British coal for Irish cattle on a pound-for-pound basis – and, finally, the dispute was settled in 1937, with virtual British acquiescence to de Valera's piecemeal overthrow of the 1922 Anglo-Irish settlement in return for a lump sum of only £10 million.

Despite adversity, the amount of 'town gas' made usually in Ireland rose from just under 5,000 million cubic feet in 1906 to almost 10,000 million cubic feet in 1939, with a corresponding rise from 134,000 to 339,000 private consumers and from 26,500 to 241,000 cookers.[99] In 1939, the president of the Association, George Anderson, was relatively content with such progress, and confessed that

> probably no period in the whole life of the gas industry has been so critical as this past thirty years which have seen the steady rise in prices; the intense growth of competition; industrial unrest, from which, I am glad to say, the gas industry has remained remarkably free, a tribute both to employer and employee; the War, with the thousand and one difficulties and troubles, which it brought with it and left in its wake; the number and magnitude of the changes and improvements which have taken place in plants and appliances and last, but not least, the change from the engineering to the commercial tone of the industry.[100]

Although coal prices had fluctuated from 12s. 6d. per ton in 1906 to 14s. 7d. in 1914, 17s. 6d. in 1916, 20s. 0d. in 1918, 55s. 0d. in 1920, and 24s. 0d. in 1938, gas prices had not increased in anything like the same proportion due to the impact of various technological advances and a growing market for coke. Labour-saving vertical retorts were introduced, for instance in Belfast and Lurgan in 1911, Bangor in 1914, Hollywood in 1917, Wexford in 1920, Derry in 1923, Dundalk in 1924, Coleraine in 1930, Limerick in 1932,

Ballymena in 1934, and Newry in 1936. Moreover, water-gas production had become general and complete gasification techniques widely known, while the vigorous adoption of the slot-meter opened the gas market to those who could not afford bi-annual payments. (In 1906, the percentage of prepayment meters to the total number of consumers was 27 percent, but by 1938 it was 68 percent.) Likewise, considerable improvements had been made in the application of gas to lighting, cooking, refrigeration, and heating. Silk, for instance, had replaced the earlier cotton or yarn in gas mantles, so that gas for public lighting was retained in Cork in 1931, Midleton in 1932, Omagh in 1933, Coleraine in 1934, Dungannon in 1935, and Warrenpoint in 1939. Indeed, competition from gas producers was so healthy that the Electricity Board for Northern Ireland had to resort to 'insidious propaganda' in 1938.

In May 1938, E. Warnock, K.C., asked the Minister of Commerce if he had seen a copy of a circular which was posted to householders in Northern Ireland purporting to be a synopsis of a book entitled *The Cause of Cancer* in which it was stated that the average gas cooker was a primary cause of cancer, and whether he had seen the statements emanating from the Imperial Cancer Research Department which described the book as a 'tissue of errors and not worth reading'. He further inquired whether the document had been circulated by the Electricity Board for Northern Ireland, whether the areas chosen for its circulation were those in which there were prosperous gas undertakings, and whether he would take immediate action to prevent further circulation of such propaganda. The Minister of Commerce replied that he had seen the documentation referred to and that the distribution of the circular by the electricity board had been confined to the Borough of Bangor. Apparently, he had already expressed to the chairman of the board his strong deprecation of that form of propaganda and secured from him an assurance that a repetition of such behaviour would not be permitted.[101] Shortly afterwards, upon his installation as mayor of Bangor, Alderman Dr. R.M. Bowman declared that such an occurrence was 'certainly a poor reward for the generous manner in which the town had handed over its electricity undertaking to the Board without looking for profit of any kind', and took the opportunity to refute the allegations and advise the citizens of Bangor 'to use the excellent gas produced by the ratepayers' own undertaking'.[102] With Bangor producing the second cheapest gas in the country, there was little danger of falling sales. However, the matter was by no means dropped in that the author of the book in question, David Brownlie, wrote to *The Gas Journal* on 17th June 1938 to contradict Warnock's contention that the Imperial Cancer Research Department had dismissed his work.[103]

Of course, there was little likelihood of major gas undertakings like

Bangor closing down in 1938. However, between 1932 and 1934, three gas concerns closed, as did eight others by 1939. Certainly, as suggested by the following table, there was positive progress in gas sales between 1934 and 1939, with a rise in gas production by more than 794 million cubic feet, and 36,835 extra consumers being served:

Gasworks	Year	No.	Make	Customers
Total	1934	73	9,092½m	302,011
Public		18	5,230m	143,862
Private		55	3,862½m	158,149
	1939	65	9,887m.	338,846
Public		17	5,515m	160,844
Private		48	4,372m	178,002[104]

However, Belfast's production accounted for four-fifths of the total gas made by local authorities as did Dublin's for two-thirds that of private gas enterprise on the island. Belfast's extra 286 million cubic feet of gas together with Dublin's 494 million accounted for practically all progress during this period! This relatively unusual success in the Irish context may have had something to do with the opening of a new sales room in Belfast in 1933 and the erection of a company theatre for public demonstrations in D'Olier Street, Dublin, in 1935. Even allowing for the demographic growth of the two cities in question, there surely had been, as *The Gas World* observed in July 1939, 'scope for more intense salesmanship and the wider adoption of such pricing methods as will induce greater usage by more general adoption of the modern appliances which inventive genius has made available',[105] outside Dublin and Belfast. Ironically enough, however, any appreciable growth before the outbreak of the Second World War would have added considerably to the difficulties suffered in securing coal and producing gas during the war.

THE SECOND WORLD WAR

On 28 September 1939 F.J. Dickens assured the shareholders of the Alliance and Dublin Gas Company that 'we are able to face the future without undue uneasiness . . . although . . . we must expect that there will be considerable restrictions . . . all precautions which would have been taken have in fact been taken and coal stocks accumulated to the limit of our storage capacity'.106 The company was certainly fortunate in having acquired in 1920 its own ships – known collectively as 'the greyhounds', or more specifically, the SS Ardri, the SS Glenageary, and the SS Glencullen.

Urban areas served by gas companies, 1934.

The *Glencree*, one of the original 'greyhounds', which operated as coal carriers for Dublin Gas Compay for many years.

The *Glencullen*, a coal carrier tied up at Dublin docks having unloaded its coal. The gasholder at Sir John Rogersons's Quay is in the background.

Nevertheless, in the very shadow of the Second World War, company stocks of coal had been depleted to a certain extent by a general strike in the port, and by a subsequent strike by the 'coal trimmers'. While the first was terminated fairly rapidly, the second lasted from September 1939 to March 1940 with the gas company eventually conceding an extra £21,000 in wages annually.

In view of the war situation, this strike was particularly interesting. Trimmers were employed to shovel the residue of the coal cargo into a position, in the holds of vessels, in which it was accessible to the mechanical devices employed in its discharge. Evidently, the men worked in gangs of eight and were paid £8 per gang per vessel. There were two gangs. One worked on vessels up to a maximum of eight in a week and the other dealt with any additional vessels that might arrive. The average individual earnings of seven coal trimmers for the year ending 5 April 1938 amounted to £386 per annum, and the gas company argued that, with £7 8s. 6d. per week, non-skilled trimmers were comparatively well-paid for labours lasting between thirty and forty-three hours a week. According to the company

> The demand that has been made is for a rate of 8d. per ton unloaded and this . . . would bring the average individual earnings to £716 per annum, or £13 15s. 4d. per week, equivalent to 9s. 2d. an hour. It is claimed that 8d. per ton is the port rate, but in fact only one other undertaking discharges by grab and the quantity handled is less than one half imported by us: if, therefore, there is a port rate, it is the rate we pay. The men's union now amend the demand by disclaiming the view that such high wages should be paid but contend that the 8d. per ton should be spread over a greater number of men resulting in average earnings for each man of £4 per week. No mention, however, has been made that this would result in the wage of £4 for working 8 hours per week equal to a rate of 10s. 0d. per man per hour.[107]

In September 1939, the gas company was determined to oppose such demands in the interests of 'our consumers, stockholders, and . . . other employers', although it realised that this would mean that its vessels would not be discharged by those operating the cranes as they belonged to the same union as the coal trimmers. In effect, this resulted in the loss of four weeks' imports at a time when every effort should have been made to improve the stock situation. It was not found possible to recover the lost ground.

Even without the coal trimmers' strike, however, it is likely that severe shortages would have been felt in Dublin. Gasworks throughout the country were seriously affected by the drastic reduction in supplies of imported coal from 1941 onwards, with the amount of gas coals supplied being hardest hit. The stoppage of coal for domestic use led simultaneously to an immediate, and unwelcome increase in the consumption of gas. As the works could only obtain limited supplies of coal – mainly of a low volatile, non-coking type – they were forced to restrict their output. In Dundalk, in 1942, gas was supplied for only five hours a day, with consumers – other than manufacturers recognised by the company – being permitted only 75 percent of the amount of gas used by them in the corresponding quarter of 1941, and all gas fires strictly prohibited. Similar reductions were made in Sligo, Cork, Galway, Wexford, Waterford, and Clonmel, while the New Northern Ireland Coal Rationing Scheme allowed consumers only 70 percent of their certified annual supply.

In Dublin there was a three-pronged approach to rationing in that there was a gradual reduction in pressure, calorific value, and fixed hours of supply, while gas undertakings in Vacan, Strabane and Roscommon shut down production because of labour or supply problems. In Dublin, house-to-house visitiations had little effect with regard to reducing consumption so that in July 1942, it was noted by *The Gas Journal* that 'certain people living on the higher levels of the city are sabotaging Dublin's gas supply . . . this black market in gas must stop. The gas position . . . is serious'.[108] Within two years, a new Emergency Powers Order made it a

" Glory be ' The Glimmer Man ! "

punishable offence to use gas in the 'off' hours or to refuse to allow an authorised officer of the Dublin Gas Company to inspect premises. As a result, there was no escaping 'the glimmer man', and much criticism of him. Typical of approaches to the question of unlawful use of gas is Bernard Share's one-sided picture in his book *The Emergency*: ' "Look out missus, here's the glimmer man!" echoed from street to street as that individual arrived, tight-lipped, to lay hands on your jets to see were they still warm. And if they were, you could expect no mercy and the bleak prospects of cold dinners'.[109] As Charles Copas, former manager in Dundalk, noted, few people remember or realise the danger of major explosions at the time because of excessive reduction of gas and the inevitable compensatory increase of air in the mains and pipes. It is, no doubt, easier to remember the human than the scientific factor.

Dishonest or disgruntled customers were not the only ones to criticise company practice. On 2 April 1941 the Emergency Scientific Research Bureau noted that the Dublin Gas Company was 'too complacent in regard to supplies of coal being made available for the enterprise and that they did not appear to visualise a situation where it would be imperative to economise'.[110] On 20 May 1942 the Bureau reported that it was not satisfied that adequate steps had been taken by the Dublin company to meet the difficulties arising out of the emergency.[111] On 14 October of the same year, it suggested that 'the possibilities of damage to retorts should not deter the company from using turf for the manufacture of gas should supplies of coal become unattainable'.[112] A month later, the accompanying question of corrosion of Dublin gas mains was dismissed by the Bureau.[113] Clearly, the Dublin company was not as willing as the Dundalk and Limerick companies to surrender vertical retorts for experimentation with turf, and not without some justification. After more than a year's work with substantial quantities of Donegal and Meath turf at Dundalk, deterioration of the silica portion of the retorts (the upper section) occurred and a number of large clinkers were found in the charcoal.[114] This was accredited by the Bureau to the high lime content of the peat ash from the Meath turf and it was duly noted that 'the obvious cure is to avoid turf of high ash content and if possible to use fireclay retorts'.[115] However, there was little chance of avoiding the main difficulty encountered in filling vertical retorts with damp turf instead of their normal diet of coal, as Leslie Channon, former manager of Dundalk, recalled during a discussion on the war years. As the shape of the vertical retorts provided for the swelling of the coal on conversion to coke as it descends, rather than the contraction of turf on conversion to charcoal, there was always a danger of explosion and/or fire in the retort house. Indeed, as the Bureau conceded, 'the volume of turf required to make a given number of therms varied from three to six times that of the coal required to make the same number of therms, while the retorts, bunkers, and conveyors of a plant designed for coal proved · inadequate when used with turf'.[116] Little wonder then, that the Limerick gasworks (which made no complaints to the Bureau and thereby secured the favourable attention of the Ministry of Industry, Commerce and Supplies)[117] was in an advanced state of deterioration by December 1946.

TURF GAS

With abundant turf reserves and experience of the operation of vertical retorts at its experimental station at Turraun bog,[118] the Bureau naturally favoured the distillation of turf even with the clogging of apparatus through the high melting point of peat tar,[119] the rejection of turf tar by Irish tar distillers, or the inevitable damage to non-fireclay vertical retorts by peat ash. It could hardly have been otherwise with severe shortages of coal, as suggested by the fact that many of the smaller gasworks using horizontal retorts – like Thurles, Mallow, Athlone, Sligo, Kilkenny and Tullamore – resorted to the use of wood or turf to supplement their meagre supplies of coal. Indeed, after 1941 many of the smaller works were forced to use more than the recommended 40 percent turf load.

Although timber suitable for use in gas retorts was scarce, some of the smaller works carbonised a certain amount of timber and derived a useful profit from the sale of wood charcoal.[120] The cooling or quenching of the charcoal on removal from the retorts was a matter of some difficlty as water quenching (as with coke) seriously damaged the charcoal and made it unsuitable for use in producers. At some works, like Thurles, airtight containers were provided in which the charcoal was allowed to cool. In Mallow, however, when a 'charge' of charcoal had been withdrawn from the retort and left on a concrete floor, charcoal dust was thrown on it so that all the glowing parts of the mass were covered with charcoal dust. The dust showed no tendency to ignite and the mass was shovelled around the floor, being turned over two or three times until there was no further danger of ignition. This process – developed by R. Barry (Town Clerk) and Mr O'Driscoll (Gas Manager of the Mallow Urban District Council's gasworks) – came to the Bureau's attention with the help of de Valera, who was sufficiently interested in the plight of the gas industry to seriously consider the possibility of erecting a gasworks on a bog and piping a supply of town gas to Dublin! The Bureau apparently humoured the Taoiseach while concentrating on the enrichment of turf gas.[121]

The use of turf for gas production was by no means impossible, as reflected by the use of turf gas, with its distinctive and lasting smell, in Athy since the early 1850s and Mullingar since the mid 1860s. Nor was de Valera the first to cast a hungry look on Irish bogs with a view to possible progress. The shift of opinion, from the view of Irish bogs as a source of land to that of energy, had begun with Sir Robert Kane as early as 1845.[122] However, little positive progress in regard to turf utilisation had been made since then in Ireland, so that F.J. Edmonds declared to the Gas Association in 1933 that 'a considerable amount of research work will be necessary before it can be used on gasworks, as, . . . it is known that the thermal yield per ton is very low . . . (and) to commercialise the use of peat one must naturally look for a financial balance sheet on the credit side of the concerns using the article'.[123] Indeed, these words were echoed in the presidential address of J.K. Cantwell in 1957 when he recalled that 'during the war years determined attempts to use turf in *conventional* gas retorts were unsuccessful both technically and economically', while pointing to the fact that 'promising processes in Sweden based on the pre-drying of turf and total gasification of turf briquettes in oxygen under pressure by the Lurgi process proved unacceptable due, principally, to high cost'.[124] Mr Cantwell, however, failed to stifle enthusiasm in this regard, for in 1958 Bord na Móna began investigating the possibility of producing town gas from milled peat with the cooperation of 'the principal Eire gas companies'. Indeed, 22,000 tons of peat were exported to the South Eastern Gas Board in London at about the same time to improve the quality of their coke.

In 1958, the Irish gas industry was already looking towards the gasification of oil rather than coal and this was not very surprising given the industry's post-war experiences. With the conclusion of hostilities on the international stage, coal supplies did not immediately improve and became so expensive that Sean Lemass declared in 1951 that 'the coal supply problem was in many ways as acute now as during the war', being different in direction but not in gravity. Furthermore, Irish gasworks were left with arrears of plant renewals and major reconstruction problems with materials of all descriptions in short supply. In some instances the deterioration had been so great that nothing less than a complete reconstruction was in order. Moreover, these financial burdens were coupled with the ever-growing demands of labour. For instance, between 1947 and 1949 there were major labour problems in Cork, Dublin, Wicklow, and Limerick. The ability of companies to quench labour unrest without making major concessions – as experienced in Dublin, Cork, Newry and Wexford at the turn of the century – had diminished to a considerable extent so that labour-relations began to occupy a great deal of time for both management and labour. This is clearly evident in a report on retort house operations made in Cork in May 1954:

171

The Dublin gas fleet of the 1930s.

A general view of Cork Gasworks in 1948 with mechanical handling vehicles in the foreground.

The Dublin gas fleet of the 1950s.

For some time, due to the attitude of members of the Gasworkers' Committee, the work in the Retort House has not been done in a satisfactory manner. Orders have been ignored or questioned and the work now no longer conforms to ordinary good practice. We have from time to time had assurances from the men and the union officials promising a change and cooperation in the future, whenever some claim or other has been conceded. Instead we have a deteriorating situation and threatened strike action every few weeks on the most trivial of pretexts. There is now no pretence to negotiation in any matter at issue but an ultimatum is delivered every time. It is not evident that these incidents are not entirely isolated but form a pattern of a planned programme to force their demands in every issue and eventually to have practical control of the works without regard to the claims of management. The tactics are to raise issues at suitable times to themselves, as on the approach of Christmas or when the Company is obliged to do something in a given time, as for instance, the preparation of a Coke cargo. . . . This conduct could have serious consequences and, indeed, the risk of serious accident to persons or plant cannot be overlooked.[125]

After a strike in May 1957,[126] the directors of the Cork gas company discussed the matter of changing over from coal carbonisation to oil gasification,[127] and decided to do so in early November 1959 for 'financial and strategic reasons'.[128] As E.J. Hobsbawn has noted in regard to Britain, 'gas manufacture was actually driven by trade union pressure to turn itself

173

into the most rapidly mechanized industry in Europe'.[129] So too in Ireland labour disputes of increasing intensity and frequency promoted an inclination towards the reduced workforce associated with oil gasification, at a time when the gas industry was only too aware of its vulnerability in the face of national and international developments.

The move away from coal carbonisation was practically inevitable given the demanding nature of traditional gasmaking procedures, with or without mechanical aids. However, the determining factor for many works was the marriage of high prices for coal with low returns for coke during the early 1950s. In 1953, for instance, the price of coal in Ireland was between four and six times the 1939 level, depending on which side of the border it was procured.[130] As a result, coke was as much as 50s. 0d. per ton more to produce in Ireland than in Britain, and was accordingly unable to compete with imports of British coke on the home market. The situation had definitely changed in favour of oil by 1953. In 1939, the average cost of coal into Irish works was less than 1d. per therm, compared with gas-oil at over 2d. per therm, and with coke valued at approximately 1½d. per therm. These margins established a firm economic reason in favour of coal distillation for base load production.[131]

By 1953, however, the utilisation of coal cost 5d. per therm in southern Ireland, which was nearly the same as the price charged for heavy fuel-oil brought from ships. Nevertheless, some works could not afford to modernise or continue gas manufacture through tried and trusted techniques. Warrenpoint, for instance closed down in May 1953, as did Cookstown in August 1956. Indeed, between 1939 and 1958, thirteen gasworks went out of operation. Progress for the remaining fifty-two works was naturally cautious for, as Jim Cantwell observed in 1957, the Middle Eastern situation forced many to reconsider the prospects of oil gasification in the context of possible shortages of oil brought about through international crises.

However, by 1962 the industry had reached the parting of the ways, with increased processing required for coal and strong competition from oil and electricity. Converging options increasingly excluded coal while promoting oil or butane/propane air for increased revenue. Indeed, this fact is amply highlighted by the situation which developed in Northern Ireland. In 1967, for instance, Bangor gas officials invited Belfast Gas Department to supply the town, after extensive renewals of the coal carbonisation plant during the late 1950s. Nor was that the only such development, for Belfast also supplied Hollywood, Lisburn, Carrickfergus, and Newtownards before it converted to oil gasification in 1965, and Coleraine served Portstewart and Portrush before its conversion to oil in 1967. Likewise, Derry converted to oil in 1965, as did Ballymena in 1967, while Enniskillen, Dungannon,

Belfast gas retort house gables from the Ormeau Road, late 1950s.

Strabane, and Omagh, for instance, had all converted to propane air by 1968.

With the development of oil gasification and processes other than coal carbonisation, it may safely be said that the gas industry's prospects were looking good in the 1960s, especially in large urban areas with an active sales team. In 1968, for instance, the change from coal to oil saved Dublin £266,000. Naturally, problems in regard to labour and competition did not evaporate for the smaller works, as suggested by the closure of twenty-two further gas undertakings by 1982. Indeed, there is a temptation to level charges of insufficient salesmanship at the old industry, and the keynote of Gas Association meetings usually involved the possibility of increased promotion through exhibition and demonstration. Certainly, increased sales between 1934 and 1939, particularly in Dublin and Belfast, were due to such policies.

However, theory and practice were not always compatible in sales as in production. The history of salesmanship in Cork provides an interesting example. A 'mobile' cooking instructor was appointed to visit customers in 1912, and cookery competitions, with prizes, organised in city schools possessing gas stoves in 1924. Indeed, in 1931, it was decided to engage 'a smart-looking lady demonstrator' to give demonstrations of gas cooking in the window of the new Patrick Street showrooms twice daily on two days per week. (The imagination and hard work evident in Dublin displays became well known to the gas community throughout the British isles, and won various responses. For instance, one window display in the Rathmines showrooms had to be withdrawn in 1948 because of objections from a Nigerian student at Trinity College, Dublin. It depicted a European being boiled in a cauldron over a wood fire somewhere in the Dark Continent, and two natives carrying a gas cooker with a placard reading 'its quicker with gas'!

However, only in 1962 was the sales situation analysed in terms of administration, presentation, competition and finance. It was admitted that natural expansion rather than promotion explained the 1930s growth in gas consumption and that this had levelled off in 1955.[132] A note of warning was given regarding the inherent dangers of an enthusiastic sales campaign which lacked an administrative back-up service. Clearly, an improvement in sales and services was necessary, as was an 'adequate showroom facility'. What was required was an increase in fitting and sales personnel, a new depot, and a new showroom which would replace No. 1, Patrick Street and No. 72, South Mall, to combine company offices with adequate space for demonstrating the performance and operation of various appliances. It was decided to proceed with care in order to meet internal and external expectations and thereby defend present sales while infiltrating fields of use other than cooking where gas could be sold with advantage. The underlying rationale was that gas accounted for as much as 80 percent of the then cooking load in the city and that the company's advancement was more likely to be in the areas of water- and air-heating, and careful internal economy. In any case, the obvious shortcomings in the sales area were compounded by the difficulty of securing satisfactory premises in Patrick Street. Only in 1970, with the purchase of Thompson's premises in Patrick Street, could the company set about doing what it had proposed in 1962. Thus, even with a well established company, progress was slow in Ireland.

THE IRISH GAS ASSOCIATION

It might well be asked, at this stage, what part the Irish Gas Association played in the overall development of the gas industry. Interestingly enough, the position looked so poor for the industry in 1945 that some members inquired as to the function of the Association.[133] They were informed that the initiative in forming the Association had been taken in Northern Ireland with the underlying reasons outlined in Mr Whimster's article in *The Gas World* of May 1886.

> It not infrequently happens that the engineer of a moderate sized, or even a small works, has single-handed to cope with difficulties which he could have easily and satisfactorily surmounted if he had had the opportunity of hearing how brethren similarly situated succeeded in their plans. The question imediately presents itself. How is it possible for men living in remote districts to gain benefit by the experience of engineers distantly removed or located in large districts of commercial activity? The plain answer is by associating together, meeting at stated intervals, and narrating peculiar modes of working and the results achieved. We have wondered why it is that Irish gas engineers have not ere now banded together for the advancement of the industry and for the improvement of their own status. It cannot be because they are not sufficiently numerous . . . nor can it be because the works they have to control are so small that a better knowledge of gas management is unnecessary. There are as many Irish gas engineers as would represent a tidy association if only one half or two thirds of them were enrolled and the insignificance of the works should be no sufficient reason for the non acquisition of knowledge. They do these things better in America. There we find engineers, with works making from ten to twenty million cubic feet per annum meeting and discussing knotty points in the manufacture of gas. There is nothing to prevent Irishmen from doing the same.

Evidently, some gas managers in Northern Ireland had tired of dealing with trouble on their own, or of crossing the Irish Sea for meetings in either England or Scotland when the industry in Ireland had shown evidence of spreading its wings. The Association was entitled The North of Ireland

Photographed during a break at the Irish Gas Association meeting in Clonmel, 1961. Left to right: N.J. Robertson, W.A. Campbell (Belfast) President-Elect; J.W. Kneeshaw, (Clonmel), President; R. Kneeshaw, father of J.W. and previously engineer at Clonmel; and W. Ainsworth, immediate past President.

Association of Gas Managers, possibly on the English model but also perhaps because its first meetings, between 1887 and 1900, were held in urban areas north of Dublin and east of the Shannon. It had a modest beginning in terms of finances and discussions, but was attended by managers throughout the country, as testified by Mr Lyne's (Wexford) repeated requests that the title of the Association be changed to the Irish Association of Managers as early as 1889. This change was eventually achieved in 1900 on the recommendations of Messrs Reid and Eustace.

Although the Association had difficulty at first in soliciting papers and securing funds, there was no shortage of material worthy of consideration for a body which refused to be simply insular in its concerns. In 1898, for instance, the subject of the 1897 Workman's Compensation Act was discussed on the recommendation of the North of England Association of Gas Managers. In 1909, the question of subscribing £5 5s. 0d. to the Livesey Memorial Fund, for the institution of a chair in gas management and chemistry in Leeds University, was considered. In 1914, H.W. Elwu related his experience of gas production in Australia. Indeed, it is interesting to note that in 1926, the Association was represented at the World Power Conference in Basel, Switzerland. The Association served both to foster an exchange of information between its members and to activate public opinion when and where required. Accordingly, it both passively reflected the state of the industry and actively influenced its development as suggested by the following instances.

Between 1919 and 1925, 'owing to the financial position of the Association', it reluctantly severed its fourteen-year-old connection with the Institute of Gas Engineers when it doubled its membership fee to ten guineas. Meetings were not held during the world wars, or 'the troubles' in Ireland. More actively, the Association emphatically protested against the Electricity Supply Bill of 1927; initiated a fund in 1936 for the widow and eight children of Maurice Drohen who lost his life through saving a retort worker in Cavan;[134] negotiated with the Ministry of Industry and Commerce regarding the Conditions of Employment Act of 1936; sympathised with M. Wilson on the closure of the Corporation Works in Tralee in 1939; and supported F.K. Thomas in his stand as gas engineer against the City Manager in Limerick in 1943.

In the early days the Association provided a social and professional outlet for managers otherwise imprisoned by the cares and duties of manufacture. There is little doubt but that they availed of the opportunity to enjoy the proceedings, at the expense of their respective undertakings. Indeed, in 1931, F.J. Edmunds appealed to certain members to be less flamboyant in their behaviour at the forthcoming dinner in Tralee!

The Irish Gas Association at the Great Southern Hotel, Killarney, 1965.

Photographed during the Irish Gas Association meeting in Killarney, 1965. left to right A.L. Allen, N.J. Robertson, W.R. Branson, J.J. O'Mahoney (President), J.A. Derbyshire, A.G. Higgins, J.M. Dow and J.J. Cantwell.

The concerns were mainly managerial. In 1918, for instance, it was proposed by the President and seconded by M.A. Kirkham that 'a letter be sent to the Chairman of every Gas Committee (if the manager of that works consents) pointing out the necessity of paying their managers at least a living wage and impressing upon the Directors or members of the Committee that they should encourage their managers to attend the Annual Conference by paying their expenses and subscriptions, which would well repay them'. In 1946, however, the scope of the organisation widened to include directors of gas undertakings and local government officials taking part in the management of undertakings, on the recommendation of F.K. Thomas.

> Mr F.K. Thomas suggested that the time had arrived to reform the Association under a new name, which he suggested should be the Irish Gas Association, with all members taking an equal part in the conduct of its affairs. He pointed out that in his opinion, the Government view of the Gas Industry was changing and that the Government now recognized that the Industry formed an important part in the economy of the country and should be developed for the benefit of the country. To assist in this development, the Association should be thrown open to directors of Gas undertakings and also to local government officials taking part in the management of undertakings.

As might be expected, there was a conservative reaction against the demolition of all distinction in 1947. This was led by H.W. Saville (Wexford) who opposed the inclusion of public officials, gas committee members etc., as members of the Association, and was supported by several speeches. Nevertheless, F.K. Thomas won the day when he expressed the view that directors and others interested in the industry should be given the opportunity to go to the Association to broaden their outlook.

The changing of the constitution again in 1983 – to accommodate developments pertaining to natural gas – was the natural culmination of this decision.

The IGA in its hundredth year is the eldest child of the gas industry on this island and, as we have seen, the fortunes of the old town gas industry varied greatly before and during the century of the Association's existence. With some degree of fortitude, both the industry and the Association have survived, and the history of the gas industry includes a wide range of elements, including human endeavour, technological progress, social and economic consequences and policital dimensions.

This book has provided a great opportunity to begin to get to know the 'gasmakers'. A continuous, methodical study remains to be done, perhaps in the broader context of the history of Ireland in the nineteenth and twentieth centuries. With the exception perhaps of Belfast and its environs, this island did not experience an industrial revolution on a European scale, and the spread of the nineteenth century town gas industry is the more remarkable for that lack of industrial context, providing a unique historical perspective which remains to be explored.

Ex fumo dare lucem, the motto of the Irish Gas Association, is an apposite expression in bringing to a close the era of the 'gasmakers'.

Epilogue
Modern Times

In its heyday in the early years of this century, the Irish gas industry supplied gas for cooking, heating and lighting in every town of any consequence, both North and South. In fact, there were as many as eighty five companies in the Twenty Six Counties and almost forty in Northern Ireland. However, the advent of electricity and its rapid decrease in cost meant that it displaced gas as the normal means of lighting, both on the streets and in homes, offices and so on.

As we have seen, gas supplies depended on complex manufacturing plant which took coal as its raw material, turning it into what by modern standards was a rather grimy and toxic domestic fuel. Manufactured 'town gas' suffered from a further economic handicap in that to supply an expanding market meant expensive investments, not only in the underground pipes needed to bring gas to new premises, but also in corresponding increases in manufacturing plant at the gasworks. In addition, because the domestic use of gas tended to peak during the day and even more so during the winter months, large volumes of gas storage were required and the expensive manufacturing plant could not be used at its full output for more than a small part of each operating hour during the year.

It was clear that if the gas industry was to survive, new and more cost-effective manufacturing technology would be needed. This became a reality in the 1950s for two unrelated reasons. Firstly, the world price of oil fell steadily in the years after the Second World War, to the point where it became competitive with coal and, because it was a liquid rather than a solid fuel, was much more convenient and easy to handle and process. The second significant development was the invention of a new chemical process by which oil could be heated and made to break up into its component chemicals, changing the liquid oil into a gas very similar to that derived from the old-fashioned coal retorts. The chemical breakdown of the oil into a

One of the two gas production platforms in the Kinsale Head field, thirty-five miles off the Cork coast, from which natural gas is brought by subsea pipeline to Inch beach in East Cork.

The construction of the onshore natural gas pipeline network is a story of Irish engineering and technological success. The first phase of pipeline construction was in the Cork Harbour area, bringing gas to the ESB, NET, Irish Steel and Cork Gas, among others. In 1982 the Cork-Dublin pipeline was extended to Limerick, Clonmel, Waterford and to specific industrial users.

useful gas was promoted by chemical agents called catalysts, in the form of finely divided metal particles, which prevented the oil undergoing the normal burning process, and yielding instead the useful domestic gas.

Thus, while competition from electricity had reduced the number of gas companies in Ireland to a handful, both North and South, the surviving companies were able to avail of the new oil-based gas technology for their manufacturing process and most town gas companies installed the new plants during the 1960s.

This enabled town gas to remain competitive for domestic cooking and space heating. However, the further fall in oil prices which occurred during the 1960s meant that householders could now install central heating rather than rely on individual fireplaces or gas fires in only a few rooms in each house. This development of oil sales for domestic heating further ate into the potential for sales of town gas.

In spite of competition from electricity and oil, as well as from solid fuel for home heating during the 1960s, the remaining town gas companies, North and South, continued with their policy of enlarging their networks to serve the new and extending suburbs around our cities and towns. The net result of this process was that until the early 1970s a very high proportion of the housing stock was piped for gas in those towns where gas was manufactured and supplied.

EVOLUTION OF THE GAS INDUSTRY OUTSIDE IRELAND

To set in context the most recent developments in the Irish gas industry, a brief diversion outside Ireland is necessary. In the 1800s and early 1900s the pattern in the United Kingdom and the rest of Europe was very similar to that described in earlier chapters. However, during the 1950s and 1960s, following adoption of the oil-based manufacturing technology referred to already, a revolutionary development took place in various parts of Europe. This involved the replacement of the cumbersome, costly and inflexible gas manufacturing process with a totally new gas coming directly from nature to the consumer – natural gas.

This revolutionary development occurred first in France early in the 1950s, based on an enormous reserve of natural gas discovered in the south-west of that country, subsequently named the Lacq Gasfield. Here the reserves were so enormous that it was soon evident that it would be economical not only to pipe the gas to the nearby cities and towns, but to extend a national network to all the large cities throughout France and particularly to Paris, many hundreds of kilometres away to the north-east. Because this new gas needed very little processing to make it suitable for use

Compressed natural gas (CNG) transporter at Waterford Glass for experimental firing of furnaces.

as a domestic heating and cooking fuel, its production rate could readily be altered to match seasonal and daily fluctuations on demand. This meant that the gas was both cheaper to acquire and cheaper to supply to the growing numbers of customers, both domestic and non-domestic. Thus, the new natural gas could compete with oil in the bulk industrial market too.

The large gas discovery in France was followed in 1959 by an even larger gas discovery in Holland, near the town of Groningen. Here the reserves were so massive that the Dutch government, having considered the possible uses of the gas, decided that the available supplies would be far in excess of the forseeable needs of Dutch homes and industries. Therefore as well as use at home, an ambitious programme of gas exports from Holland to Germany, Belgium, France, Switzerland and Italy was initiated. Thus began, in the early 1960s, the linking together of all the gas industries of mainland Europe into what has now become the EuroGas Grid. So, the gas industry evolved from isolated manufacturing units into an integrated supply system.

Following the discoveries of gas in France and Holland, geologists began to ponder the possibilities of finding gas in the North Sea off the coast of Holland, following the geological trend which had produced gas onshore. The Dutch have not been particularly successful in finding gas in their offshore area, with only a few small finds there. However, in 1966 in the United Kingdom sector of the North Sea, the first of a long line of gas and oil discoveries was made. As was the case in mainland Europe, the piping into Britain of this new natural gas radically transformed and integrated the gas industry there to the point where natural gas now supplies one third of all the energy consumed in the United Kingdom and almost two-thirds of total domestic energy needs. And, in 1986 the gas industry in the United Kingdom, under the unified British Gas Corporation, has been privatised and sold to the public for a massive £5.6 billion. How far removed from the grimy old gasworks image!

IRELAND ENTERS THE NATURAL GAS ERA

The rather unlikely and totally unforseen development of natural gas resources in mainland Europe and the North Sea led to speculation about the possibility of similar gas resources in Ireland. While we had all been taught as children that Ireland possessed no natural resources of any consequence, mineral and metal discoveries in Ireland in the 1950s posed a severe challenge to these earlier beliefs. Exploitation of minerals generally and oil and gas were controlled by various Acts of the Oireachtas, and the Mines and Minerals Act of 1958 made a specific reference to the possibility of the development of oil and gas resources and the various controls that would be appropriate to such development — leasing terms, technical regulations and so on.

Welding operations on an Irish Gas spurline during the summer of 1986.

One of two compressed natural gas (CNG) road tankers which provide a constant supply of gas to industrial uses distant from a pipeline route.

Whether stimulated by the 1958 Act or by the significant developments elsewhere in Europe, there were some brave souls who felt it worthwhile to speculate on the possibility of oil and gas reserves in Ireland. Thus, in 1958, an exclusive licence to explore for oil and gas was granted to the Ambassador Oil Company. However, so little was known about the potential for oil and gas discoveries at that time that the consideration for the granting of this licence is believed to have been a nominal sum.

Exploration Onshore Ireland

The Ambassador Company, armed with its exclusive licence to explore for oil and gas throughout Ireland, set about the task in the conventional manner. The first stage was to study the available geological and geo-physical data, which was meagre enough. It was then necessary to carry out seismic exploration by which the underground strata likely to contain oil or gas could be located. This involved detonating explosive charges set into the ground in a regular pattern and recording the shock waves bounced off the various rock layers underneath. As a result of this exploration work during the 1960s, a number of exploratory wells were drilled in counties Meath, Clare, Cavan, Cork and Leitrim. With the exception of a small show of gas in the well drilled near Dowra, Co. Cavan, no oil or gas was found.

As is the custom with oil exploration licences throughout the world, the Ambassador Oil Company, which originally held 100 percent of the exclusive licence, decided during the 1960s to sell off parts of its interest. This is how the Continental Oil Company (Conoco) and later the Ohio Oil Company (now renamed Marathon Petroleum) bought into the exploration licence. Following the unsuccessful onshore work, Marathon subsequently acquired 100 percent of the licence in 1966.

Because of the developments in the North Sea and in other offshore areas, national governments decided that they would take charge of the economic rights in their offshore areas, as well as onshore, and this led to the tricky business of defining the 'median line', setting the boundary of these 'economic interests' between countries. For example, the median line half way across the North Sea, separating the United Kingdom and Norwegian economic interests, was later found to bisect the large Frigg gasfield, and a subsequent redefinition of the median line in this case, using satellite surveying techniques, resulted in the line being shifted by a few metres, and causing changes in ownership of gas worth billions of pounds.

In Ireland's case, Marathon negotiated an extension of their exclusive exploration licence to cover a significant part of Ireland's offshore area. In 1969, they concluded a further agreement with the Irish authorities which allowed them to explore an area of some 17,000 square miles off our coast, over a period of twenty years. The available area would reduce every five

A CNG road tanker filling at the roadside compressor station.

Natural gas fuel tanks at an individual customer's site.

192

years so that after the twenty-year period, the exploration rights would revert to the state, save in those areas where Marathon had carried out drilling and thereby earned the right to retain the drilled offshore blocks for further development. Thus it was that in 1970, Marathon began seismic work offshore, in an area off our south coast.

Offshore Exploration – the Kinsale Head Gasfield

Oil or gas exploration offshore is considerably more expensive than onshore. This is because every activity undertaken in exploration and production must be carried out in a hostile environment using ships which today cost anything from $20,000 per day to hire and operate. As a result of the initial seismic survey, Marathon decided to drill several areas about thirty miles off the coast of Cork. In September 1971, one of these exploration wells, the third in the series, struck gas in Block no. 48/25-2 some twenty-seven miles south of the Old Head of Kinsale in about three hundred feet of water. They had found the Kinsale Head Gasfield.

Further exploratory drilling delineated the full extent of the geological structure containing the gas and it was subsequently proved that the Kinsale Head Gasfield contained over one trillion cubic feet of natural gas of very high quality. To give some idea of how much gas this is, the gasfield today produces more energy than the combined output of the Electricity Supply Board and Bord na Móna. The total gas reserves found by Marathon, at mid-1980's prices, are valued at £6 billion.

PUTTING NATURAL GAS TO WORK FOR IRELAND

Marathon's exploration licence allowed them to bring any gas or oil ashore and sell it at the best price available. It must be remembered that at the time of the discovery of the Kinsale Head Gasfield, in the early 1970s, energy prices were many times lower than at present. Thus, the economics of an extensive pipeline system to distribute gas throughout Ireland were unfavourable. So it was that Marathon considered selling gas only in the greater Cork area immediately adjacent to a prospective landfall for a pipeline ashore from the Kinsale Head Gasfield. It was estimated at that time that the field was capable of producing 125 million cubic feet per day of gas for a twenty-year period. A short survey in the Cork area suggested that not more than one-tenth of this amount of gas could be absorbed by existing Cork energy users, even if all of them were to change over to natural gas. Thus it was in August 1973 that Marathon suggested to the government that they might arrange for new large gas-using projects to be undertaken in the Cork area, so that the full output of the field could be absorbed and the

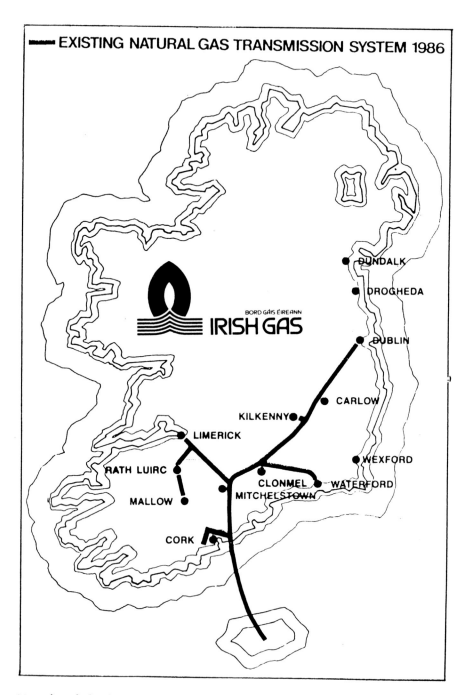

EXISTING NATURAL GAS TRANSMISSION SYSTEM 1986

BORD GÁIS ÉIREANN
IRISH GAS

DUNDALK
DROGHEDA
DUBLIN
CARLOW
KILKENNY
LIMERICK
WEXFORD
RATH LUIRC
CLONMEL WATERFORD
MITCHELSTOWN
MALLOW
CORK

Natural gas fuel tanks at an individual customer's site.

expensive offshore capital investment rendered financially viable. Following some study, the government decided early in 1974 that the output from the gasfield should be allocated to a new ammonia plant to be built by NET, the state fertiliser company, as well as to two new power stations to be built in the Cork area for the ESB, the national electricity authority. It was later decided to set up a state gas authority which would sell the gas piped ashore by Marathon to these two bodies as well as to any other customers who might be allocated a gas supply. Bord Gáis Éireann – the Irish Gas Board – was established under the Gas Act of 1976, with responsibility for the purchase and sale, transmission and distribution of natural gas throughout Ireland. The first customer identified in addition to ESB and NET was the Cork Gas Company, which distributed manufactured town gas to some 27,000 customers in Cork city.

Following the various energy crises of the 1970s, it was considered that more extensive use should be made of natural gas and in 1978 it was decided that the gas should be used to promote new industrial projects, particularly those which would regard the availability of natural gas as a special attraction to locate or set up in Ireland.

The major energy market in Ireland, particularly for premium energy supplies, is of course located in the greater Dublin area, with its high concentration of offices, factories and commercial undertakings of all kinds, as well as one-third of the nation's homes. But piping natural gas 140 miles from Cork to Dublin would undoubtedly be a major undertaking. Thus it was that a succession of feasibility studies was carried out in the late 1970s and early 1980s. Then, in 1982, the decision was taken by government that natural gas should be piped to Dublin and distributed there by the Alliance & Dublin Consumers' Gas Company. Without the new supplies of gas, the Dublin Gas Company, as it was popularly known, would undoubtedly have had to discontinue supplying gas to its 160,000 customers. Indeed, the massive capital expenditure involved in the changeover from manufactured to natural gas has proved so difficult that in 1986, the Dublin Gas Company was put into receivership and is now being reorganised and financially restructured.

The Cork-Dublin pipeline, built in 1982, was conceived as the backbone of a national gas system. During 1983 and 1984 extensive discussions took place with the Northern Ireland authorities with a view to a contract for supplying natural gas from Dublin to Belfast and the other surviving gas companies in Northern Ireland. Although these negotiations completed their final stages, the Northern Ireland Authorities finally declined to sign a gas supply contract and this project has been suspended. Nevertheless, the town gas utilities in Northern Ireland, notwithstanding their impending close-down, are still endeavouring to secure a supply of natural gas, possibly from the now privatised British Gas Corporation and, if not, to resurrect the North/South project.

Meanwhile, a number of spurs have been taken off the Cork-Dublin pipeline to serve the towns of Limerick, Waterford, Clonmel, Kilkenny and Carlow and also to supply a number of large industries and co-ops adjacent to these pipelines. Plans are well advanced for a gasline north from Dublin as far as Dundalk to serve the residential, commercial and industrial energy users in north Dublin, Meath and Louth. This pipeline will in part be aided by the European Regional Development Fund and may later be extended to serve energy users in some of the other counties south of the border, to offset the considerable economic difficulties under which enterprise in this area must operate.

The gas industry in Ireland has a long and proud tradition of service to homes, offices and factories throughout the country. We have seen its evolution from the provision of street lighting to home lighting, to home cooking and eventually space and water heating in the home. On the supply side, the original coal-based manufacturing process gave way to the more modern oil-based manufacturing processes, which helped to keep the industry in business for a few years. The oil crises of the 1970s faced the industry with extinction, which was averted only by the advent of natural gas. Now the revitalised industry can look forward to a renewed lease of life in the service of its many thousands of customers throughout Ireland and as a key component of our national energy policy.

Notes

PREFACE

1. See, for instance, J.J. Lee, 'Irish Economic History since 1500', in *Irish Historiography 1970-79*, edited by Joseph Lee (Cork University Press, 1981); or L.A. Clarkson, 'The writing of Irish economic and social history since 1968', in *Economic History Review*, XXXIII (February 1980) pp. 100-11.

2. See, for instance, Hayes's *Guide to Sources for the History of Irish Civilisation*, (Boston, 1970).

3. In 1892, for instance, the Board of Trade sent out 526 questionnaires to gasworks throughout the United Kingdom, related to numbers employed and wages paid. Only 60 percent of the forms were returned as required (*The Tyrone Courier*, 3 September 1892.) In 1918, the President of the Irish Association of Gas Managers reported that only fifty-one replies were received in answer to the 109 letters sent out to discern the state of the industry.

4. Richard Kavanagh, 'Energy', in *A Profit and Loss Account of Science in Ireland*, edited by P.E.M. Clinch and R. Charles Mollan (Royal Dublin Society, 1983) pp. 49-66.

5. Trevor I. Williams, *A History of the British Gas Industry* (Oxford University Press, 1981) p. IX.

6. J.M. Cohen & M.J. Cohen, *The Penguin Dictionary of Quotations* (Penguin Books, 1960) p. 81 (12).

7. R.F. Delderfield, *God is an Englishman* (London, 1970) p. 262.

CHAPTER ONE

1. Walter T. Layton, *The Discovery of Gas Lighting*, (Walter King: London, 1926) p. 39.

2. Ibid., p. 18.

3. Ibid., pp. 22-3.

4. Malcolm W.H. Peebles, *Evolution of the Gas Industry*, (Macmillan Press Ltd: London, 1980) p. 7.

5. Susan E. Messham, *Gas: An energy industry*. (Her Majesty's Stationary Office, 1976) p. 2.

6. Peebles, *op. cit.*, p. 7.

7. Messham, *op. cit.*, p. 3.

8. Ibid., p. 2.

9. Ibid., p. 2.

10. Peebles, *op. cit.*, p. 8.

11. T.I. Williams, *A History of the British Gas Industry*. (Oxford University Press, 1981) p. 4.

12. Ibid., p. 4

13. Ibid., p. 4

14. Sterling Everard, *The History of the Gas Light and Coke Company, 1812-49*. (Ernest Benn Ltd.: London, 1949) p. 14.

15. Ibid., p. 4.

16. Messham, *op. cit.*, p. 2.

17. E.J. Hobsbawn, *Industry and Empire* (Penguin Books, 1969) p. 41.

18. T.I. Williams, *op. cit.*, p. 8.

19. Ibid., p. 8.

20. Ibid., p. 15.

21. James Stelfox, from a paper '*A description of Belfast Gas Works*' (July, 1896).

22. Peebles, *op. cit.*, p. 15.

23. For an interesting treatment of meters, see O.K. Smyth, 'Meters – The gas man's secret weapon' in *Gas Engineering and Management* (October, 1984).

24. Williams, *op. cit.*, p. 124.

25. Robert K.G. Temple, *China: Land of Discovery and Invention*. (Patrick Stephens, Wellingborough: London, 1986) p. 78.

26. Ibid., p. 52.

27. Dean Hale (ed), *Diary of an Industry, American Gas Journal*, 1970. No pages given, see under 1775.

28. Ibid., see under 1821.

29. Peebles, *op. cit.*, p. 54.

30. Dean Hale, *op. cit.*, see under 1885 and 1890.

31. Report on the Nature and Products of the process of the Destructive Distillation of Peat, made to the Right Honourable the Chief Commissioner of Woods by the Director of the Museum of Irish Industry. (W. Clowes & Sons: London, 1851) p. 509.

32. *The Freeman's Journal*, 4 March 1824.

CHAPTER TWO

1. Malcolm Peebles, *op. cit.*, p. 10-11.

2. By 1822, two gas companies had been formed in Dublin, one in Belfast and one in Newry. By 1846, there were three gas companies in Dublin, two in Clonmel and Limerick, and one each in Ballymena, Belfast, Dungannon, Coleraine, Carlow, Derry, Drogheda, Dundalk, Kilkenny, New Ross, Newry, Wexford, Galway, Sligo, Cork, Mallow, Tipperary, Youghal, Armagh, and Waterford. By 1856, there were two gas companies in Dublin and Limerick, and one in Antrim, Armagh, Ballymena, Ballymoney, Ballynahinch, Banbridge, Bangor, Belfast, Carlow, Carrickfergus, Cashel, Castleblayney, Castlederg, Cavan, Clonmel, Coleraine, Cookstown, Cork, Derry, Downpatrick, Drogheda, Dromore, Dundalk, Dungannon, Enniskillen, Galway, Hillsborough, Keady, Kilkenny, Larne, Lisburn, Lismore, Lurgan, Mallow, Monaghan, Nenagh, New Ross, Newry, Newtownards, Newtown-Limavady, Omagh, Portadown, Portaferry, Sligo, Strabane, Tipperary, Tralee, Wateford, Wexford, and Youghal. By 1881, there are two gas companies/works in Downpatrick, Cookstown, Lisburn, Limerick and Naas; and one in Antrim, Ardee, Armagh, Athlone, Aghnacloy, Athy, Ballina, Ballinasloe, Ballymena, Ballycastle, Ballymoney, Ballynahinch, Ballyshannon, Banbridge, Bandon, Bangor, Belfast, Bagnalstown, Balbriggan, Birr, Boyle, Bray, Cahir, Cashel, Carlow, Cavan, Carrickfergus, Carrickmacross, Castleblayney, Carrick-on-Shannon, Castlebar, Clones, Coleraine, Clonmel, Cork, Cootehill, Derry, Donaghadee, Drogheda, Dromore, Dungarvan, Dungannon, Enniscorthy, Ennis, Enniskillen, Fermoy, Galway, Gorey, Hollywood, Kells, Kilkenny, Kinsale, Larne, Letterkenny, Limavady, Lismore, Longford, Lurgan, Mallow, Maryborough, Midleton, Monaghan, Moy, Mountmellick, Mullingar, Navan, Nenagh, New Ross, Newport, Newry, Omagh, Newtownards, Portadown, Portaferry, Portrush, Queenstown, Randlestown, Rathfryland, Roscommon, Skibbereen, Strabane, Sligo, Tanderagee, Tipperary, Roscrea, Thurles, Tralee, Tramore, Tullamore, Trim, Tullow, Tuam, Warrenpoint, Waterford, Westport, Wexford, Wicklow, Youghal, Kingstown, Hillsborough and Keady.

3. PRONI, Belfast, D.642/191.

4. *The Cork Examiner*, 17 August 1972.

5. Ibid.

6. In 1805, *The Cork Mercantile Chronicle* declared: Our total indifference in this city to everything which concerns our public accommodation and credit has become a subject of wonder. Our nuisances seem to have a procreative power and every day seem to show some vexatious instance of their abominable fecundity. The day traveller runs the risk of being blinded from the screening of lime, he is often intercepted in his way by the lagoons of water which the obstruction of the public sewers retain in the streets and if he be not rode over by the gallopers who charge along the streets or driven over by the cars which are whirled along with no less rapidity, he may felicitate himself on his return home upon the cheap terms of such injury as he may have received in tumbling over a few of the many heaps of rubbish which principally occupy our public ways. If the traveller by night escapes drowning he has no right to complain for what with the darkness of the lamps and the naked and unfenced state of the quays to survive a night walk has become a matter of family thanksgiving. Every stranger who approaches this 'the third city in his Majesty's dominion' does so at the peril of his life.

7. *The Freeman's Journal*, 8 January 1819.

8. *Dublin Historical Record*, XIV, p. 60.

9. *The Cork Examiner*, 18 January 1901.

10. P.R.O.N.I., Belfast, Problems of a Growing City: Belfast 1780-1870, 1973.

11. *The Cork Morning Post*, 24 February 1816.

12. *The Freeman's Journal*, 9 April 1819.

13. *Technology Ireland*, September 1975, p. 68.

14. *The Freeman's Journal*, 2 May 1822.

15. Ibid.
16. Ibid. 7 August 1824.
17. Ibid. 18 February 1819.
18. Ibid., 25 February 1819.
19. Ibid., 1 March 1821.
20. Ibid., 25 October 1822.
21. Ibid., 21 January 1824.
22. Ibid., 25 October 1822 and 21 January 1824.
23. Ibid., 10 February 1865.
24. Ibid., 10 February 1865.
25. Ibid., 21 August 1844 and 1 October 1844.
26. Ibid., 10 February 1865.
27. Ibid., 25 May 1865 and 4 January 1845; *The Cork Examiner*, 21 March 1859.
28. See Tim Kelly, 'Ennis in the nineteenth century'. M.A. thesis, U.C.G., 1971.
29. *The Freeman's Journal*, 17 October 1826.
30. *The Cork Examiner*, 24 September 1856.
31. *The Freeman's Journal*, 8 August 1844.
32. Ibid., 2 August 1844.
33. Ibid., 8 August 1844.
34. Ibid., 10 August 1844.
35. Ibid., 2 August 1844.
36. Ibid., 21 August 1856.
37. *The General Advertiser*, 21 September 1844.
38. *The Freeman's Journal*, 1 October 1844.
39. Ibid., 21 August 1844.
40. *The Cork Examiner*, 6 January 1845.
41. *The Cork Morning Post*, 2 March 1825.
42. *The Cork Examiner*, 23 May 1856.
43. Ibid.
44. *Cork Constitution*, 22 May 1856.
45. ibid.
46. Ibid., 16 September 1856.
47. Ibid., 21 March 1857.
48. *The Cork Examiner* 9 November 1856; 5, 10 and 19 September 1856: 27 August 1856.
49. Ibid., 1 December 1856.
50. Ibid., 4 and 13 November 1872.
51. *Cork Constitution*, 21 March 1857.
52. *The Cork Examiner* 29 December 1856 and 8 September 1858, 31 December 1856.
53. Ibid., 19 December 1856.
54. *Cork Constitution*, 21 March 1857.
55. *The Cork Examiner*, 13 May 1859.
56. Ibid., 30 May 1859.
57. Ibid., 13 May 1859.
58. Ibid., 21 March 1859 and 5 September 1859
59. Ibid., 5 September 1859.
60. *Kilkenny Journal*, 16 October 1847.
61. *The Cork Examiner*, 13 May 1859.
62. Cork Gas Company Minutes, 30 March 1860.
63. *The Cork Examiner*, 26 September 1856.
64. *Cork Constitution*, 26 August 1856.
65. George Anderson, 'A History of the Cork Consumer Gas Company and its Engineer', available in the company's premises, Patrick Street; Also in H. Still's memoirs p. 88.
66. *The Freeman's Journal*, 10 February 1856.
67. Clonmel Deeds of Settlement (1844) available in the P.R.O., Dublin and the local museum, Clonmel.
68. *The Cork Examiner*, 27 May 1856 and 3 September 1858; *The Freeman's Journal*, 21 August 1856.
69. Limerick Corporation Minutes, December 1879 (special meeting).
70. *Limerick Reporter*, 20 February 1841.
71. Limerick Corporation Minutes, 1 February 1875 (special meeting).
72. Ibid.
73. *The Cork Examiner* 17 September 1856. *Limerick Reporter* 6 November and 17 August 1849.
74. Limerick Corporation Minutes, 6 July 1876.
75. Ibid., 11 December 1877.
76. The Alliance & Dublin Consumers' Act (1847).
77. *The Irish Times*, 29 February 1864. *The Freeman's Journal*, 10 February 1865.
78. Ibid., 10 and 11 February 1865.
79. Ibid., 10 February 1865.
80. *The Dublin Builder*, 1 August 1864.
81 *The Freeman's Journal*, 14 February 1865.
82. Ibid., 31 March 1865.
83. Ibid.
84. Ibid., 25 May 1865.
85. Ibid., 29 May 1865.
86. Ibid., 8 August 1844.
87. Ibid., 25 May 1865.
88. *The Dublin Builder*, 1 October 1866.
89. Ibid., 15 December 1866.
90. *The Irish Builder*, 15 November 1871.
91. Ibid., August 1871.
92. Ibid., 15 April 1872.
93. Ibid., 1 November 1872.
94. Ibid., 15 December 1872.
95. Ibid., 1 November 1872.
96. Ibid., 15 December 1872.
97. Ibid., 15 May 1873.
98. P1134, National Library Dublin, Section 1.
99. Ibid., Section 2.
100. Ibid., Section 3.
101. Ibid.
102. ibid., Section 4.

103. *The Freeman's Journal*, 25 March 1876.

104. Ibid., 25 February 1876.

105. See, *The Freeman's Journal*, 1 and 3 March 1876.

106. Ibid., 29 February 1876.

107. Ibid., 26 February 1876.

108. Ibid., 1 March 1876.

109. Ibid., 3 March 1876.

110. *The Irish Builder* 1 September 1879 and 1 August 1881.

111. Ibid., 1 May 1874.

112. Ibid., 1 May 1874.

113. Ibid., 1 September 1874.

114. Ibid., 1 June 1878.

115. Ibid., 1 November 1878.

116. Ibid., 1 July 1879.

117. Ibid., 15 May 1881.

118. Ibid., 1 August 1882.

119. Ibid., 1 June 1878.

120. Ibid., 15 December 1874, and 1 March and 1 December 1875.

121. Ibid., 15 January 1879.

122. Ibid., 1 December 1879.

123. Ibid., 1 January 1882.

124. Ibid., 1 January 1878 and 1 February 1879.

125. Ibid., 15 April 1880 and 1 May 1875.

126. Ibid., 1 December 1875, 1 February 1879 and 15 February 1879.

127. Ibid, February 1879.

128. Ibid., 15 July 1883.

129. Ibid., 1 October 1877.

130. *The Newry Telegraph*, 12 April 1881.

131. *The Wexford Freeman*, 16 April 1836.

132. Ibid., 7 May 1836.

133. *The Galway Mercury*, 11 October 1845.

134. *The Sligo Champion*, 13 August 1881.

135. *The Tyrone Courier*, 10 January 1885.

136. Ibid., 7 February 1885.

137. *The Tuam Herald*, 29 May 1879.

138. *Wexford Constitution*, 24 November 1860.

139. *Kildare Observer*, 14 October 1882.

140. *Tuam Herald*, 9 July 1881.

141. *Drogheda Argus*, 21 February 1885.

142. *Carrickfergus Freeman*, 13 May 1865.

143. Ibid., 18 November 1865.

144. *The Sligo Champion*, 20 August 1881.

145. *Down Recorder*, 23 November 1878.

146. *The Newry Telegraph*, 8 September 1877.

147. *Down Recorder*, 23 November 1878.

148. Ibid., 26 October 1878.

149. See Cornelius O'Leary, 'Government in the Age of Reform' in *The Town in Ireland*, edited by David Harkness and Mary O'Dowd, Historical Studies XIII, (Appletree Press, 1979)

p. 196. Also see, *The Freeman's Journal*, 22 June 1855.

150. *The Journal of Gas Lighting*.

151. *The Kildare Observer* 21 February 1880; 13 and 20 March 180.

152. *The Newry Telegraph*, 6 December 1881.

153. *The Tipperary Advocate*, 17 April 1860. Ibid., 16 June 1860.

154. *The Kilkenny Moderator*, 22 October 1845.

155. Teresa Kelly, 'Carlow Gas Works', *Carlorian* (1961).

156. *The Galway Vindicator*, 30 March 1859.

157. *The Londonderry Standard*, 1 September 1853.

158. *The Carlow Sentinel*, 23 December 1848.

159. *The Irish Times*, 21 March 1865.

160. *Cork Morning Intelligence*, 24 February 1816.

161. *Wexford Herald*, 3 January 1832.

162. *The Dublin Builder*, 15 February 1861, 1 June and 1 July 1859.

163. *The Irish Times*, 9 March 1860.

164. Ibid., 29 November 1861.

165. *The Westmeath Independent*, 22 March 1851.

166. Announcement of meeting in Westport, Hoban Printers, 10 June 1857.

167. *Westmeath Guardian & Longford Newsletter*, 30 October 1851.

168. Ibid., 9 October 1851.

169. 'Gas Poisoning in Dublin', paper by E.J. McWeeney read in the Section of State Medicine in the Royal Academy of Medicine in Ireland, on 22 April 1904.

170. See, for instance, *The Freeman's Journal* 21 May 1859 and 27 June 1855; and *The Irish Times* 4 January 1860.

171. 'Practical Rules for the Management of Gas for Artificial Light' by a gas fitter and apparatus maker of twenty years' experience. J. Magee & Co., (London, 1857).

172. *The Cork Examiner*, 10 December 1891.

173. Ibid., 26 January 1893.

174. *Drogheda Argus*, 21 February 1885.

175. *The Coleraine Chronicle*, 6 September 1905.

176. *The Cork Examiner*, 16 November 1856.

177. *The Journal of Gas Lighting*, 2 July 1889.

178. *Kilkenny Journal*, 11 August 1847.

179. *The Cork Examiner*, 24 November 1856.

180. *The Irish Times*, 12 February 1863.

181. *The Dublin Builder*, 15 June 1864.

182. *The Downpatrick Recorder*, 19 January 1878.

183. *The Waterford News & General Advertiser*, 8 May 1885.

184. *The Larne Observer*, 3 August 1906.

185. The Memoirs of Henry Still, Cork Gas, p. 40.

186. Dundalk Gas Company Minutes, 11 November 1859.

187. *The Cork Examiner*, 20 and 24 January 1893.

188. Cork Company Minutes, 24 November 1860 and 10 August 1861.

CHAPTER 3

1. Minute Books of Board Meetings, Cork Gas Consumers' Company, 16 May 1901.

2. *The Cork Examiner*, 20 May 1901.

3. Ibid., 20 May 1901.

4. Ibid., 20 May 1901.

5. Ibid., 20 and 21 May 1901.

6. Ibid., 1 March 1901.

7. Ibid., 28 February 1901.

8. Ibid., 28 February 1901.

9. Ibid., 1 March 1901.

10. Ibid., 20 May 1901.

11. Ibid., 21 and 22 May 1901.

12. Ibid., 3 to 10 June 1901.

13. Police Reports, Co 904/73, September 1901, p. 401. Minute Books, *op. cit.*, 7 September 1901.

14. Ibid., 23 March 1901.

15. *The Cork Examiner*, 4 June 1901.

16. Minute Books, *op. cit.*, 17 August 1861.

17. Ibid, 5 April 1862.

18. Ibid., 8 February 1862.

19. Ibid., 29 November 1862.

20. Ibid., 21 December 1861.

21. Ibid., 25 April 1863.

22. Ibid., 20 July 1867.

23. Ibid., 22 July 1867.

24. Ibid., 22 July 1867.

25. Ibid., 22 July 1867.

26. Ibid., 24 November 1867.

27. Ibid., 22 August 1868.

28. *The Cork Examiner*, 13 November 1872.

29. Company Minutes, *op. cit.*, 11 Oct. 1871.

30. Ibid., See 28 April 1866.

31. Ibid., 19 October 1861.

32. Ibid., 21 April 1866.

33. Ibid., 4 and 7 November 1871; 6 July 1872; and 27 January 1872.

34. Memoirs, *op. cit.*, pp. 41, 49, 50, 53, 57-9, 62.

35. Minute Books, *op. cit.*, 3 December 1859.

36. The Memoirs of Alfred Henry Still, 1809-1901, p. 37. Presented to the Cork Gas

Company by Gwyenth Still.

37. Ibid., pp. 29-30.

38. Ibid., p. 31.

39. Minute Books, *op. cit.*, 19 October 1861.

40. Ibid., 15 September 1893.

41. Memoirs, *op. cit.*, 45-6.

42. Minute Books, *op. cit.*, 18 March 1858.

43. *The Cork Examiner*, 5 January 1892.

44. Dundalk Gas Company, Report Book, 4 November 1891 and 6 April 1893.

45. *Western Star & Ballinasloe Advertiser*, 12 November 1870.

46. *Roscommon Journal & Western Advertiser*, 19 November 1887.

47. Clonmel Corporation, Gas Committee, Minutes, 20 September 1901.

48. Minutes of the Wexford Gas Consumers' Company, 1918/9.

49. Ibid., 5 June 1865.

50. Ibid., 5 June and 21 October 1865.

51. Ibid., 30 July 1866.

52. Ibid., 8 December 1865.

53. Ibid., 16 July 1869.

54. Ibid., 28 December 1869.

55. Ibid., 15 and 19 July 1918.

56. Ibid., 26 July 1918.

57. *The Wexford People*, 4 January 1919.

58. Wexford Company Minutes, *op. cit.*, 'Labour Troubles', November 1918.

59. Ibid., November 1918.

60. Ibid., November 1918.

61. *The Wexford People*, 4 January 1919.

62. Minute Books of the Dundalk Gaslight Company, 14 July 1856.

63. Ibid., 15 August 1856.

64. Ibid., 28 October and 14 December 1856.

65. Ibid., 15 August 1856.

66. Ibid., 29 June and 21 July 1886.

67. For further information on Dundalk Gas Company, see, for instance, *The Tempest Annual* for 1925 and 1974; and the more recent work done by Ogra Dun Dealgan, Chapel Street, Dundalk. Some of this material was published in *The Argus*, 31 October 1986.

68. Dundalk Company Minutes, *op. cit.*, 1 October 1891.

69. Ibid., 27 August 1892.

70. P.R.O., Belfast, D.1761/1/1, 6 and 14 July 1869.

71. Ibid., 12 April 1872.

72. Ibid., 16 April 1872.

73. Ibid., D.1761/1/2, 7 March 1882, 13 March 1882, 1 October 1883, 5 August 1884 and 31 July 1885.

74. Ibid., D.1733/1/2, June 7 1893, 13 August 1894, and January 28 1895.
75. Ibid., 25 February 1895 and October 28, 1896, 28 June 1897, February 22 1909, and 27 January 1911.
76. Ibid., 22 February 1909.
77. Ibid., D.1400, 12 September 1863 and 14 November 1863.
78. Ibid., 2 December 1866.
79. Ibid., 11 October 1898.
80. Ibid., 9 October 1865.
81. Ibid., 2 February 1879.
82. Ibid., D.2240/1, 29 January 1877.
83. Ibid., 18 April, 10 and 21 September 1878.
84. Ibid., 1 October 1879.
85. Ibid., 15 October 1879 and 31 January 1882.
86. Ibid., D.2565/1/1, 25 August 1866.
87. Ibid., 22 October 1870.
88. Ibid., 22 October 1870.
89. *The Cashel Gazette*, 8 January 1881.
90. Ibid., 15 January 1881.
91. Ibid., 8 January 1881.
92. Ibid., 18 December 1880.
93. Ibid., 8 January 1881.
94. The Minutes of the Cork Gas Company for 4 May 1951 record that: Mr Sheehan reported that Mr. Moynihan, Works Chemist, had been appointed Manager of Clonmel Gas Works and had given a month's notice of his intention to leave.' For further information on this controversial appointment, see *The Clonmel Chronicle* for the period in question.
95. *The Derry People*, 15 November 1902.
96. P.R.O., Belfast, D.2223/33/1.
97. Ibid.
98. *The Tuam Herald*, 15 February 1890.
99. *The Kildare Observer*, 10 November 1899.
100. *The Fermanagh Mail & Enniskillen Chronicle*, 4 November 1886.
101. P.R.O., Belfast, D.2565/1/1, Gas Works Regulations, October 1851.
102. Ibid., Mic. 159, 17 March 1855.
103. Ibid., D.1400/1, 23 September – 15 October 1872.
104. Dundalk Company Minutes, *op. cit.*, 27 August 1856.
105. Ibid., 2 December 1856.
106. Clonmel Minutes, *op. cit.*, 6 December 1901.
107. Ibid., 10 December 1901.
108. Ibid., 9 January 1902.
109. Ibid., 30 January 1902.
110. Ibid., 30 January 1902.
111. P.R.O., Belfast, D.1750/1/1, 1848.
112. *The Carlow Post*, 12 April 1862.
113. *The Cork Examiner*, 28 July 1858.
114. For the use of Methylated Spirits and the avoidance of leakages through frost, See *Newry Telegraph* 18 January 1881.
115. Cork Company Minutes, *op. cit.*, 27 October and 3 November 1860.
116. Ibid., 3 November 1860.
117. Ibid., 11 January 1862.
118. Ibid., 16 December 1871.
119. Ibid., 6 January 1872.
120. Ibid., 16 July 1881.
121. P.R.O., Belfast, D.1761/1/2, 4 April 1888.
122. Ibid., D.770.
123. Ibid., D.1750/1/4A, 10 December 1903.
124. Ibid., D.2565/1/3, 6 April 1899.
125. Ibid., 19 and 29 March 1899.
126. Ibid., 6 April 1899.
127. For the regulations governing supply by the British Gas Light Company in Clonmel, see Document (Acc. No. 1984: 403) in the Clonmel Museum.
128. *The Londonderry Journal*, 8 February 1831.
129. *The Dublin Builder*, 15 January 1866.
130. *The Irish Builder*, 15 July 1874.
131. P.R.O., Belfast, D.2223/33/1.
132. Ibid., D.1761/1/2, 1 April 1896.
133. Information courtesy Dave Burke, Cork Gas.
134. Also see, *The Argus*, 31 October 1986.
135. 'Carlow Gas Works' by Teresa Kelly in *Carlorian* (1961) p. 18.
136. *The Down Recorder*, 11 February 1911.
137. Information contained in a letter in Clonmel Museum.
138. *The Irish Times*, 21 March 1864.
139. Information courtesy of Leslie Allen, formerly Dublin Gas, March 1849.
140. Ibid., April 1852, September 1852 and January 1854.
141. Ibid., March 1849 and 1854.
142. Dundalk Company Report Book, 4 November 1891.
143. Ibid., 4 November 1891.
144. Ibid., 5 February 1890.
145. All the following references may be found in the Minutes of the Wexford Gas Company.
146. Cork Company Minutes, *op. cit.*, 6 September 1884.
147. Ibid., 4 October 1895.
148. *The Freeman's Journal*, 29 May 1865.
149. *The Coleraine Chronicle*, 8 April 1905.

150. Ibid., 8 April 1905.

151. Ibid., 8 April 1905.

152. J. Taylor to R. Kneeshaw 22 Sept. 1911.

153. Letter to the Chairman and Members of the Clonmel Gas Committee from J. Prendergast, John Morrissey, W. Peters, James O'Gorman, T.L. Gynn and Pat Gibbons, 5 September 1911.

154. R. Kneeshaw to the Chairman and members of the Gas Committee, 28 Sept. 1911.

155. H.W. Saville to R. Kneeshaw, 1 September 1911.

156. J.E. Enright to R. Kneeshaw, 23 September 1911.

157. B. Mitchel to R. Kneeshaw, 18 Sept. 1911.

158. Corporation Minutes, *op. cit.*, 25 September 1912.

159. P.R.O., Belfast, D.770.

160. Ibid. D.770.

161. *The King's Country Chronicle*, 29 April 1886.

162. P.R.O., Belfast, D.1733/1/2.

163. *The Cork Examiner*, 17 February 1887.

164. Kinsale Gas Co. Balance Sheet, 30 June 1887.

165. *Kilkenny Journal*, 7 September 1898.

166. *The Newry & Belfast Standard*, 7 Jan. 1898.

167. Cork Company Minutes, *op. cit.*, 7 September 1872.

168. *The Cashel Gazette*, 8 January 1881. For other instances of violence at the works, see, for instance, *The Evening Telegraph* 24 December 1907, and Dundalk Company Minutes for 4 February 1892.

169. P.R.O. Belfast, D.1761/1/2, 6 October 1897.

170. Statistics of Gasworks compiled in Clonmel in 1899.

171. Ibid.

172. Cork Company Minutes, *op. cit.*, 28 January, 4 and 25 February 1971.

173. See, *The Dublin Builder*, 15 April 1861.

174. Patrick D. Molumby, 'Lighting Dublin', *The Capuchin Annual* (1973) p. 80.

175. Ibid., p. 80.

176. P.R.O., Belfast, D.1750, 5 October 1853.

177. Clonmel Corporation Minutes, *op. cit.*, January/February 1901.

178. *The Down Recorder*, 12 August 1911.

179. *The Coleraine Chronicle*, 6 May 1905.

180. Ibid., 6 May 1905.

181. Cork Company Minutes, *op. cit.*, 1 April 1871.

182. *The Lisburn Herald*, 18 May 1909.

183. See, *Western People* 13, 20 and 27 April 1983 for a detailed account of gas distribution etc.

184. *The Lisburn Herald*, 9 September 1905.

185. Navan Lighting Committee Minutes, 25 February 1908.

186. *Dungannon News*, 9 September 1899.

187. *Londonderry Standard*, 7 March 1886.

188. *The Clare Saturday Record*, 18 July 1890.

189. Clonmel Minutes, *op. cit.*, 16 Oct. 1896.

190. *The Cork Examiner*, 5 January 1892.

191. *The Carrickfergus Advertiser*, 18 Oct. 1907.

192. P.R.O., Belfast, D.770.

193. Ibid.

194. *The Londonderry Standard*, 29 Dec. 1853.

195. P.R.O., Belfast, D.770.

196. 'Practical Rules for the Management of Gas for Artificial Light', J Magee & Co., London, 1857. (Trinity College, Library, Dublin.)

197. Ibid.

198. Ibid.

199. *The Freeman's Journal*, 31 January 1906. Lecture given by Professor A. Roche in the College of Science, Stephen's Green, Dublin.

200. Ibid.

201. *Belfast Evening Telegraph*, 14 Nov. 1893.

202. J. Emerson Reynolds, 'Recent Analyses of the Dublin Gas Supply and Observations thereon', Scientific Proceedings, Royal Dublin Society, 12 May 1900; and E.J. McWeeney, 'Remarks on the cases of Carbon Monoxide Asphyxiation that have occurred in Dublin since the addition of Carburetted Water-gas to the ordinary coal-gas, Scientific Proceedings, Royal Dublin Society, 27 October 1904.

203. *Cavan Weekly People*, 26 January 1901.

204. *The Gas Journal*, 18 July 1928.

205. Cork Company Minutes, 22 Feb. 1895.

206. *Cavan Weekly News*, 8 June 1901.

207. Belfast P.R.O., D.2223/33/4. R.B. Bailie to Colonel R.H. Wallace, 29 November 1913.

208. Ibid., D.2223/33/4.

209. *The Down Recorder*, 10 July, 1926.

210. *The Irish Times*, 9, 10, 13 and 14 March 1945.

211. Cork Company Minutes, *op. cit.*, 15 April 1871.

212. *Belfast and Newry Standard*, 6 March 1885.

213. *Ballina Herald*, 22 October 1927.

214. *The Fermanagh Mail & Enniskillen Chronicle*, 27 September 1886.

215. *Kilkenny Journal*, 26 February 1898.

216. *Mid Ulster News*, 11 February 1899.

217. Cork Company Minutes, *op. cit.*, 11 December 1858.

218. Ibid., 30 December 1858.

219. *Cashel Gazette*, 9 October 1880.

220. Cork Company Minutes, *op. cit.*, 11 January 1862.

221. *The Cork Examiner*, 13 November 1872.

222. Information supplied by Dave Burke, Cork Gas.

223. *The Cork Examiner*, 10 June 1901.

224. *The People*, 11 February 1882.

225. *Dungannon News*, 20 July 1899.

CHAPTER 4

1. *The Irish Times*, 9 May 1860.

2. *The Downpatrick Recorder*, 19 January 1878.

3. Carlow: *The Irish Builder*, 1 May 1878.

4. Naas: Ibid., 1 May 1878.

5. Enniskillen: *The Fermanagh Mail and Enniskillen Chronicle*, 4 November 1886.

6. Drogheda: *The Irish Builder*, 1 May 1878.

7. Portadown: *The Ulster Gazette*, 10 October 1908 and 12 September 1908.

8. Derry: *The Ulster Examiner*, 3 May 1877.

9. Dungannon: *Portadown News*, 5 July 1900; see also: *The Dungannon News*, 9 March 1899, 20 July, 1899, 10 August 1899, 7 September 1899, 5 October 1899, 4 January 1900, 5 July 1900; *The Mid Ulster Mail*, 8 July 1899, 9 September 1899.

10. Lisburn: *The Lisburn Herald*, 9 January 1909.

11. *The Ulster Examiner*, 10 November 1877.

12. Teresa Kelly, *op. cit.*, p. 19.

13. List compiled by the Clonmel Gas Company.

14. *Kilkenny Journal*, 6, 13 and 27 August 1898.

15. *The Ballina Herald*, 15 September 1928.

16. Navan Minutes, *op. cit.*, 11 and 25 February 1908.

17. *Mid Ulster Mail*, 8 July 1899.

18. *Journal of Gas Lighting, Water Supply and Sanitary Improvements*, 22 July 1884, 7 October 1884, 21 October 1884, 10 February 1885, 8 September 1885, 6 October 1885, 24 April 1888, 16 March 1886, and 23 March 1886.

19. Ibid., 10 April 1888.

20. Ibid., 8 April 1883, 22 May 1883, 29 May 1883, 19 June 1883 and 10 April 1888.

21. *The Portadown News*, 9 December 1899.

22. *The Kildare Observer*, 9 September 1899.

23. *The Irish Builder*, 1 May 1878.

24. *The Carrickfergus Advertiser*, 5 April 1907.

25. Ibid., 20 August 1907.

26. Ibid., 30 August 1907.

27. The Sunlight Gas Company Ltd., System of Purified Acetylene Gas Lighting. Printed by Cherry & Smalldridge, Seville Works, Dublin. Available in the National Library, Dublin.

28. *The Irish Times*, 30 April 1863, and The *Ulster Gazette*, 29 August 1908.

29. *Derry People*, 10 January 1902.

30. *The Impartial Reporter & Farmer's Journal*, 13 November 1902.

31. Ibid., 13 November 1902.

32. *Dungannon News*, 14 December 1899.

33. See, Slater's Directory for the year 1897.

34. *Sligo Independent*, 1 April 1899.

35. *Tyrone Courier*, 8 August 1885.

36. *The Tuam Herald*, 12 November 1887; *The Clare Saturday Record*, 12 September 1891; *The Cork Examiner*, 5 January 1892; and *The Wicklow Newsletter & Arklow Reporter*, 11 February 1905.

37. *The Drogheda Conservative Journal*, 28 October 1848.

38. *The Downpatrick Recorder*, 19 October 1878.

39. *The Irish Builder*, 15 December 1878.

40. Ibid.

41. Ibid., 1 March 1879.

42. Ibid.

43. *Journal of Gas Lighting*, 2 August 1881.

44. *Portadown News*, 9 December 1899.

45. *The Journal of Gas Lighting and Sanitary Improvement*, 3 May 1881.

46. Maurice Manning & M. McDowel, *The History of the Electricity Supply Board*, (Gill & Macmillan, 1984) p. 7.

47. See, for Waterford, the Report of the Proceedings of the 30th Annual General Meeting of the Irish Association of Gas Managers, 13 August, 1918.

48. Cork Company Minutes, *op. cit.*, 26 November 1881.

49. Ibid., 23 December 1881.

50. Ibid., 28 January 1881.

51. Ibid., 8 October 1881.

52. Ibid.

53. *Journal of Gas Lighting*, 28 February 1882.

54. See, for instance, *The Cork Examiner*, 9 July 1962 and 29 November 1976; and *The Evening Echo* 6 January 1975.

55. Article by Denis Gwynn, entitled 'Now and Then, published in *The Cork Examiner* sometime in 1955 and provided courtesy of Dave Burke, Cork Gas.

56. Hand-written document in the possession of Cork Gas.

57. *The Journal of Gas Lighting*, 6 October 1891.

58. Maurice Manning & M. McDowel, *op. cit.,* Ch. 1.

59. See, for instance, *The Dungannon News*, 9 March 1899, and *The Down Recorder* 11 March 1911

60. *Journal of Gas Lighting*, 18 October 1892.

61. *The Ulster Gazette*, 15 February 1908.

62. Navan Minutes, *op. cit.*, 25 February 1908.

63. Ibid., 19 April 1911.

64. Ibid., 26 November 1919.

65. *The Tuam Herald* 1 and 8 December 1888.

66. *The Lisburn Herald*, 10 June 1905.

67. *Coleraine Chronicle*, 10 May 1924.

68. *Irishman*, 2 July 1870, quoted in Sean Daly's *Cork: A City in Crisis, 1870-2.* (Tower Books: Cork, 1978), p. 56.

69. *Journal of Gas Lighting*, 25 May 1886.

70. Clonmel Minutes, *op. cit.*, 18 January 1904.

71. Wexford Minutes, *op. cit.*, 31 March 1916.

72. Ibid., 16 March 1917.

73. P.R.O., Belfast, D.1400/4; *Newtownards Chronicle & Co. Down Observer*, 7 September 1918.

74. *Newtownards Chronicle*, 10 December 1921; 7 and 14 January 1922.

75. Ibid., 14 January 1922.

76. Ibid., 11 March 1922.

77. Presidential Address of A.I.G.M., 1929.

78. Cork Company Minutes, *op. cit.*, 16 October 1917.

79. Ibid., 17 May 1915.

80. Ibid., 20 May, 14 and 28 October 1918, and 8 March 1926.

81. Denis G. Marnane, *Land and Violence: A History of West Tipperary from 1660*, (Fitzpatrick Bros., Tipperary, 1985) Part III.

82. Cork Company Minutes, *op. cit.*, 14 March and 24 March 1924.

83. Ibid., 8 May 1922, 20 July 1925, 15 October and 3 December 1923.

84. Ibid., 10 September 1923.

85. Ibid., 12 February 1923.

86. Dundalk Minutes, *op. cit.*, 14 August 1925.

87. Ibid., 21 July 1926.

88. Cork Company Minutes, *op. cit.*, 2 January 1922.

89. Wexford Company Minutes, *op. cit.*, 23 March 1928.

90. *The Gas World*, 7 August 1935.

91. Ibid., 8 October 1932.

92. Ibid., 7 October 1933.

93. Ibid., 20 August 1932.

94. Ibid., 21 January 1933.

95. Ibid., 30 August 1932.

96. Ibid., 17 August 1935.

97. Ibid.

98. David Johnson, *The Interwar Economy in Ireland*, Studies in Irish Economic and Social History, (Dundalgan Press, 1985) p. 15.

99. *Gas Journal*, 2 August 1939.

100. *Gas World*, 20 July 1939.

101. *Gas Journal*, 25 May 1938.

102. Ibid., 1 June 1938.

103. Ibid., 22 July 1938.

104. *The Gas World*, 20 July 1939.

105. Ibid., 20 July 1939.

106. Printed bi-annual reports for Dublin Gas, 28 September 1939.

107. Ibid.

108. *Gas Journal*, 24 July 1942.

109. Bernard Share, *The Emergency: Neutral Ireland, 1939-45.* (Gill and Macmillan, 1978) p. 13.

110. Minutes of Meetings of the Emergency Scientific Research Bureau, 2 April 1941.

111. Ibid., 20 May 1942.

112. Ibid., 14 October 1942.

113. Ibid., 4 November 1942.

114. Report of Activities by the E.S.R.B., 1941-5. File 309A, p. 22.

115. Ibid., p. 22.

116. Ibid., p. 22.

117. Minutes E.S.R.B., *op. cit.*, 4 February 1942.

118. File 309A, *op. cit.*, p. 16.

119. Ibid., p. 18.

120. See *The Irish Times* 4 June 1942 for a report from S. Lemass to the effect that there were between 600 and 611 vehicles in the country operating from gas producer plants.

121. Minutes E.S.R.B., *op. cit.*, 23 September and 21 October 1942.

122. Kavanagh, op. cit., p. 51.

123. *The Gas World*, 19 August 1933.

124. Ibid., 25 May 1957.

125. Cork Company Minutes., *op. cit.*, 17 May 1954.

126. Ibid., 8 May 1957.

127. Ibid., 20 May 1957.

128. Ibid., 5 November 1959.

129. E.J. Hobsbawn, *op. cit.*, p. 190.

130. *The Gas World*, 20 September 1953.

131. Ibid.

132. Cork Company Minutes, *op. cit.*, 15 August 1962.

133. Irish Gas Association Minutes, courtesy of Mrs Pam MacSwiggan.

134. See *The Gas World*, 15, 22 and 29 February 1936.